The Hyderabad Heist

Sharmishtha Shenoy is the author of the *Vikram Rana Mystery* series, which include *Vikram Rana Investigates, A Season for Dying, Behind the Scenes, Fatal Fallout, Silent Witness, A Thousand Scars: Book 1* and *A Thousand Scars: Book 2*. She has also published a book of short stories, *Quirky Tales*, and the novel *Murder in the Chowdhury Palace*.

Sharmishtha has an M. Tech degree from the University of Reading, Great Britain. Before starting to write, she was an IT professional and worked for TCS, Satyam, Infosys and Microsoft. She is a big foodie and enjoys biryani (both Hyderabadi and Awadhi versions) and rasgullas, like most Bengalis. She is also a lusty bathroom singer. Though she is happily married to Mr Shenoy in real life, in her fantasy world she is wedded to her fictional creation Vikram Rana.

You can read more of her writing on her blog: https://sharmishthashenoy.com/bulletin-board/

Sharmishtha lives in Hyderabad. You can reach her at sharmishtha.shenoy@gmail.com

The

The Untold Story of India's

Hyderabad

Biggest Museum Theft

Heist

SHARMISHTHA SHENOY

RUPA

Published by
Rupa Publications India Pvt. Ltd 2023
7/16, Ansari Road, Daryaganj
New Delhi 110002

Sales centres:
Allahabad Bengaluru Chennai
Hyderabad Jaipur Kathmandu
Kolkata Mumbai

P-ISBN: 978-93-5520-984-9
E-ISBN: 978-93-5520-985-6

First impression 2023

10 9 8 7 6 5 4 3 2 1

Dedicated to
The Hyderabad Police—the Covid warriors

CONTENTS

FOREWORD

I was introduced to Sharmishtha Shenoy's work when she gave me a copy of her crime thriller *Murder in the Chowdhury Palace*. What struck me even more than Sharmishtha's vivid imagination was her utter lack of pretension. Her honesty made her writing not only accessible but also relatable because beneath all the thrill and drama, there were recognizable human characters and emotions. The same holds true of this book, a true-crime story about a theft that occurred at The Nizam's Museum, Hyderabad, Telangana, in September 2018.

Neither is this book just about good storytelling nor is it a figment of the author's imagination. It is a story about the hard work, intelligence and determined spirit of the Hyderabad Police, which I consider to be the best police department in the world.

Because most museum theft cases are never solved—the one famous case that was solved was the theft of the *Mona Lisa* from the Louvre Museum in 1911—the Hyderabad Police achieved a momentous feat when it solved this case within 10 days. It was an honour and privilege to head the group of professional police officers working on this case. I feel that this book is the perfect opportunity to highlight the professional work put in by my team to solve The Nizam's Museum theft case.

Background

On 3 September 2018, Hyderabad was rocked to its core when The Nizam's Museum was robbed in the dead of the night. Several expensive, antique heritage artefacts, studded with diamonds, emeralds and rubies, were stolen. As the commissioner of Hyderabad Police, I arrived at the crime scene along with senior police officers to investigate the matter.

For the Hyderabad Police, this case was not about the theft of small items with practically little to no value. Today, the value of these stolen artefacts is worth over ₹50 crore. Further, their monetary value was not the crucial aspect. This crime was the theft of our heritage and culture. The artefacts stolen from the museum were gifts given by rulers across the world to the seventh Nizam of Hyderabad on his golden jubilee in the year 1937. This gave the entire Hyderabad Police enough impetus to swing into action. Such a sensational case was not only a challenge for me but also something in which the state government was heavily invested because it was a loss of heritage for the people of Telangana.

The story has been the same from the first crime ever committed, which may have been simple and rudimentary, to the most advanced cybercrime being tackled by law enforcement agencies now. The strategies, tactics, philosophies, mind games, one-upmanship and cat-and-mouse chase between a criminal and a police officer have continued. In many cases, a police officer has to get into the mind of a criminal and put himself in the criminal's shoes to successfully solve a crime. What goes on in the mind of a criminal? What inspires him? What motivates him? What pushes him to plan and commit a crime? These questions have been the subject of many studies, books and movies. Yet, we do not have a conclusive answer. We only know that crime evokes interest. Does this interest stem from the fear factor? Or is it because crime evokes curiosity?

In my 30 years of service, one thing I have observed is that criminals are groomed by circumstances. Sometimes, they create these situations themselves. From the time when humans were hunter-gatherers to the contemporary time of blue-chip technology, a section of society has always been attracted to crime. They think of it as an easy option. The police exist to counter crime. As a proud khaki-wearing police officer, I consider this profession to be one of the most challenging, satisfying and inspiring on earth.

In my youth, I remember reading *Crime and Punishment* by Fyodor Dostoevsky, the prolific Russian author. As my young and impressionable mind meandered into the world of crime presented by Dostoevsky, I never knew that one day, I would be solving crimes and handling criminals. While reading this book, I learnt that Dostoevsky had to spend four years in a Siberian labour camp, as the Czar of Russia had imprisoned him there. I remember being really upset about it. I was equally upset to read about the pathetic conditions of police stations in Russia in those days. In the early part of my career, my visits to police stations always reminded me of this masterpiece.

I started my career as the Assistant Superintendent of Police in Jangaon in the erstwhile Warangal district of Telangana in 1990. The condition of police stations like Narmetta, Maddur, and Bacchanapet was not good. We are fortunate that the present government, under the leadership of Sri K. Chandrashekar Rao, has done so much to improve the quality of policing and working conditions of our department. The Hyderabad Police department is the first in the country to have over 900 patrol cars and 2,000 patrol bikes for crime prevention in the city.

⌒

If you step into the world of criminals, you will find that, for them, crime is normal. It's just their way of life. I have seen criminals who have been sentenced to five, even seven, years of jail and on the day of their release, even before heading home, they commit a fresh crime. Reform or punishment has been debated and discussed for a long time.

On 2 June 2014, the Chief Minister of the youngest state of India—Telangana— mentioned that law and order and the prevention and detection of crime would be the top priority of the new government.

As the commissioner of police, I was the kotwal of the city and took it as a personal challenge to keep it crime free. The kotwal has been a long-standing institution, perhaps the oldest in the country. Even during the Mughal times, every big city used to have a kotwal who was incharge of law and order and the prevention of crime. Many European writers and travellers have spoken about the kotwal being an essential pillar of the Nizam's administration. It also finds a reference in the great book *Ain-i-Akbari*, which talks about the institution of the kotwal during Akbar's time.

Secunderabad, for a long time, remained under the control of the British, and the jurisdiction of the kotwal of Hyderabad did not extend to Secunderabad. It was only in 1945 that the British Resident allowed Secunderabad to come under the direct control of the kotwal of Hyderabad. In 1957, the Hyderabad City Police was modernized and reorganized for the first time on a large scale, when the city was divided into four divisions (now called zones): North, South, East and West.

The City Armed Reserve (CAR) police are one of the oldest police organizations within the Hyderabad City Police. It was established in 1932 with the name 'Afghan City Police' and stationed at Petlaburj Police Lines. In 1957, it was renamed the CAR. The reason I bring the CAR into the picture is to express my gratitude to them for making a valuable contribution to this case. They sometimes escort our police officers and provide us armed cover when we go for sensitive operations. I want to thank the Additional Commissioner of Crime Ms Shikha Goel, the Additional Deputy Commissioner of Police Taskforce Mr Chaitanya and Inspector K. Madhu Mohan Reddy. It was due to their wholehearted efforts that we recovered the heritage of Hyderabad.

Anjani Kumar (IPS)
Former Commissioner, Hyderabad Police

PROLOGUE

Like a slippery snake, Ghulam wriggled in through the narrow ventilator on the terrace of The Nizam's Museum, Hyderabad. Once he was inside the museum building, holding on to the ventilator, he swung his feet and kicked the CCTV camera placed directly underneath, damaging it. He had a rope tied around his waist, the other end of which was held by Badshah, his friend and distant cousin, who was crouching by the ventilator. Ghulam nodded to Badshah, who gradually started lowering him into a well-lit room of the museum. As soon as his feet touched the ground, Ghulam quickly undid the rope from his waist and hurried to the display unit holding a gold tiffin box studded with diamonds. Breaking the pathetic single lock of the unit was a piece of cake for him. The lock made a slight noise as it gave way. Nervously, he looked around to check if anybody had been alerted. The museum remained silent and still. His eyes glinted in appreciation as he gently opened the display case, without making any further noise, and held the tiffin box in his hands. He had been dying to do this since he had seen it for the first time, a few weeks back.

He glanced around to double-check that nobody had been alerted. Then, he picked up the gold cup and saucer studded with emeralds and rubies next to the tiffin box. He was carefully placing the tiffin box, the cup and the saucer inside his rather shabby duffel bag when he remembered the shiny gold spoon with a single emerald embedded in its handle. He quickly grabbed it and put it in the bag as well.

Next, he went to the unit with the Holy Quran inside a gold box. The moment he was about to break the lock, the azaan started playing in a nearby masjid. The sound of the azaan made him feel as if a bolt of lightning had struck him, so much so that he shivered in apprehension. It seemed to him like a personal rebuke from Allah for his misdeeds. It also made him realize that it must be past 5.00 a.m. It would soon be light. He and Badshah needed to get away quickly. He rapidly retraced his steps and tied the rope around his waist.

Badshah, who had been watching Ghulam through the ventilator, whispered to him urgently, 'Take it, take it!'

'*No Ustaad, paap lagega* (No bro, God will curse us),' Ghulam responded.

'*Arre kuch nahi hota* (Nothing will happen)!' Badshah said again, a little more loudly.

'Shh! Somebody will hear! It's already past 5.00 a.m. Soon, everybody will wake up. Let's go! Pull me up!' Ghulam hissed in a low, panic-stricken voice.

Badshah started pulling the rope swiftly. Soon, Ghulam emerged out of the ventilator on to the terrace. Using the torch of their SIM-less cell phone to light their way, they rushed across the terrace, clambered up a ladder to the terrace of the next building, and from there, silently climbed across to the roof of the residential building that abutted onto the wall of the museum.[1] Swiftly and silently, they raced across the roof of the residential building, retracing the path they had taken to enter and rob the museum. They stealthily ran down the stairs of the residential building. It was still dark, and most people were sleeping despite the azaan. The two men reached the front of the masjid next to the residential building, where they had parked their bike. Ghulam took out the cell phone from his pocket and pretended to make a call in front of the masjid, fully aware that his activities were being recorded by the CCTV camera on the roof of the masjid. After that, they sped away on their unmarked bike.

Ghulam and Badshah spent the next few hours moving around in various parts of Hyderabad. They had removed their masks after moving out of the area and now looked like two ordinary youths riding their bike, although they were sweating nervously, expecting the police to arrest them at any moment. They felt jubilant and tense at the same time. This had been their biggest heist so far, something they had never in their wildest dreams thought that they would be able to pull off.

They eventually decided to head back to their place in Rajendra Nagar. When they finally reached the safe haven that was Badshah's house, they hugged each other, laughing aloud in relief as the tension gradually left their exhausted bodies.

They did not know it yet, but they had just created history by committing the first-ever multi-million-dollar heist in Hyderabad at The Nizam's Museum. This case would baffle the

---

[1] As told to the author by the current curator of The Nizam's Museum and police officials, there are various residential buildings whose walls abut the museum. There are no gaps and all the Greater Hyderabad Municipal Corporation rules are flouted. The administrators of the museum have complained about this but to no avail.

police and would go on to become one of the most sensational and prominent cases in the 30-year career of Anjani Kumar, the commissioner of the Hyderabad Police.

1

THE DISCOVERY OF THE THEFT

Monday, 3 September 2018

Gaurav, a vlogger, was waiting with his girlfriend, Pia, for The Nizam's Museum to open. He had planned to shoot a video tour of the museum and upload it to YouTube. Pia was doubling as his cameraperson. Even though the rainy season was officially over, it had rained in the early morning, and the grounds were wet, the grass green and the weather still quite pleasant. He deeply breathed in the petrichor. He knew it would be hot soon, but for now, it was just perfect. He had deliberately chosen Monday, since the museum tended to be less crowded on that day. Also, Janmashtami fell on 2 and 3 September that year, and because of the festive occasion the number of visitors would be pretty less. Further, their early entrance would ensure there were even fewer visitors around.

The museum was located right at the end of the grounds of the Purani Haveli—the official residence of the Nizam. Visitors were allowed entry to the museum grounds only. There were two wings on either side of The Nizam's Palace. The left wing housed the museum and a school. The right wing housed a women's college. On that day, both the school and college were closed for Janmashtami, though the museum itself would soon open to the public.

While waiting for the ticket counter to open, Gaurav thought he would try to film himself near the actual palace of the Nizam. He strolled casually towards the ground marked 'Private'. From there, he could see glimpses of the imposing white mansion, the Purani Haveli.

Gaurav had thoroughly researched the place before going there. He knew that the haveli, which is a masterpiece of eighteenth-century architecture, had witnessed the childhoods of at least two Asaf Jahi rulers. Princess Durru Shehvar, the eldest daughter-in-law of the seventh Nizam, used to reside there whenever she visited Hyderabad. He also planned to inform his audience in his vlog that the property is owned by a trust and no one has resided in the palace since Durru Shehvar's death. Prince Muffakham Jah, one of Princess Durru Shehvar's sons, divides his time between London, Turkey and Hyderabad and resides in a private mansion in Banjara Hills while in Hyderabad.

As Gaurav and Pia walked closer to the mansion to get a better view, a security guard walked up to them, his boots crunching against the gravel. 'Where are you going?' he asked Gaurav quite aggressively, staring at him suspiciously.

'*Arre mia*, I am going to film The Nizam's Museum and upload it on my YouTube channel. I am just filming the background of the museum for this,' Gaurav explained.

'This is a private property. Filming not allowed here. Go back,' the security guard said, waving his hands at Gaurav as if he was swatting a fly.

The Purani Haveli (recently restored exterior)

Source: The Hyderabad Police

'*Arre bhaiyya*, do you have any idea how many subscribers I have on YouTube? 1.9 lakh! This museum will be seen by millions of people across the world. It will bring more visitors to your museum. And I am just filming the mansion and explaining how the museum was created. What's wrong with that?' Gaurav reasoned.

But the guard seemed least impressed and refused to let Gaurav go even a step further. His argument about the vlog helping promote tourism had fallen on deaf ears. Muttering under his breath about the uncouth and illiterate security guard, Gaurav retraced his way back to the museum with Pia.

As time went by, Pia started getting bored and fidgety. To distract her, Gaurav suggested, 'Let us start with the background story of the Purani Haveli. Hopefully, the museum will open by the time we finish shooting this part. Remember, your camera should cover both the wings of the palace, and then you will show the main ground of the Nizam's residence. Unfortunately, we can't film the actual residence. That bloody guard—'

'What do you mean by "wings"?' Pia interrupted Gaurav's rant.

The wing housing The Nizam's Museum
Source: Sharmishtha Shenoy

'Arre, the row of white buildings on both sides of the ground, ending in that magnificent white building, where the Nizam's family used to stay,' Gaurav explained, pointing at the white building housing the museum.

Pia stifled a yawn and picked up the camera. She was getting quite bored with Gaurav and his enthusiasm for vlogging. She knew she would need to end the relationship soon. She was pursuing a master's in physics from Osmania University and planned to go overseas for her doctorate.

Unaware of Pia's thoughts and plans, Gaurav started speaking in front of the camera. 'Hello guys! Today I am taking you all on an exciting tour of The Nizam's Museum. In the heart of the Old City of Hyderabad, a fascinating collection of articles belonging to the seventh Nizam of Hyderabad, Mir Osman Ali Khan, is on public display at the museum.

'The building is locally known as Purani Haveli. It is also known as Masarrat Mahal and as Haveli Khadeem, which means old mansion. It was the official residence of the Nizam and was constructed for Sikander Jah, Asaf Jah III, by his father Ali Khan Bahadur, Asaf Jah II.[2] The museum in this building was opened to the public on 18 February 2000 by The Nizam's Jubilee Pavilion Trust, which Prince Muffakham Jah, the youngest grandson of the last Nizam, heads. The museum showcases the fascinating collection of gifts that were presented to the last Nizam, Mir Osman Ali Khan, Bayafandi Asaf Jah VII, on the occasion of the silver jubilee of his rule in 1937.

'Though he completed 25 years of rule in 1936, the joyous occasion was celebrated in 1937. This was because Princess Victoria of the United Kingdom, the fourth child and second daughter of King Edward VII and Queen Alexandra, and the younger sister of King George V, died in December 1935. Out of respect to the deceased princess, one year was allowed to pass before the Nizam's jubilee celebrations commenced.

'The seventh and the last Nizam himself registered these articles in 1957 to display them to the general public. There are over 1,000 objects in the museum, of which only 400 are on public display.

'There are, at present, more than 10 buildings in the Purani Haveli. The main building, where the Nizam family used to reside, is flanked by two long parallel wings. The museum also has a collection of dresses worn by the sixth Nizam. By all accounts, he was extremely fashion-conscious and had an extensive collection of tasteful and high-quality clothes. It is

---

[2]'Purani Haveli', *Hyderabad Guide*, https://bit.ly/3ztPKaT. Accessed on 31 October 2022.

also rumoured that he never repeated his clothes; once worn they were put away. In fact, he used to buy the entire bale of the cloth from which his clothing was made and destroy the extra cloth so that there would be no other dress available in the same material.'

By the time Gaurav finished speaking, the museum had opened, and the couple bought their tickets for entry. The museum itself was located on the second floor, and they had to climb up a wooden staircase to reach it. Pia was impressed by the beautiful red staircase, as was Gaurav. He breathed in the faint musty smell of the old museum appreciatively. He was fond of old and beautiful things and felt proud that he was from Hyderabad, the land of the Nizams. Though the wooden staircase was ancient, it hardly creaked as they climbed up.

'So old and yet the staircase is intact. Just look at the quality!' Gaurav exclaimed in awe.

Once inside the museum, they started recording again and went through the various silver artefacts, including replicas of the famous Moazzam Jahi Market and Osmania University. Soon, they moved to the third hall, which housed the section containing the gold ornaments.

Gaurav was waxing eloquent about a gold model of the Jubilee Hall[3], when Pia let out a muffled scream, interrupting his flow. She nearly dropped her camera as she raised a trembling finger and pointed at an empty display unit, its doors wide open.

Gaurav, too, gaped at the display unit and exclaimed, 'Oh my God! There has been a theft here!'

---

[3]Jubilee Hall is a marble structure in the Public Gardens close to the Assembly building in Hyderabad.

2

SHOCK AND PANIC

Pia's scream jerked Farhan, the museum attendant, awake from his nap. He had been sitting on a stool in the long corridor outside the display room, dozing off. He was not feeling well and his legs were aching. There were few visitors at this hour, and some that were wandering around did not stay long enough to arouse his interest or register in his memory.

Farhan rushed inside to see what had happened. Gaurav saw the guard and pointed at the empty display unit, saying, 'Look, somebody has stolen some items!'

Farhan, too, gaped at the open door of the unit. His blood ran cold. He was responsible for cleaning the museum and checking that everything was fine before opening it to the public. The previous day, the museum had been closed to visitors for Janmashtami, and the floors were more or less clean. So, he had not bothered to clean up the third hall before unlocking the door for the public. How he wished he hadn't been so lazy. The cupboard was not immediately visible from the doorway of the third hall. If only he had gone inside the hall and checked the display units, he would have noticed the open cupboard. Now, the curator and the administrator would know that he had not done his due diligence. Worse still, they might think he had committed the theft. By this time, other security guards had rushed in too, including the head of security, Rizvi.

To save himself, Farhan blurted, 'Everything was fine when I opened the hall and checked the cupboards. These people must have done something.'

Gaurav and Pia were taken to the curator's office, where they were frisked. 'Why would we inform the guard if we were the ones who had stolen the items?' Gaurav asked, infuriated. His arguments fell on deaf ears.

The curator, Kalam, immediately closed the museum. Luckily, there were no visitors other than Gaurav and Pia. Kalam, then, called the administrative officer of the Nizam's estate, Bilal. Kalam's voice shook with tension as he spoke. 'Bilal, I am sorry to say that there has been a theft at the museum.'

'*Ya, Allah!*' Bilal exclaimed. He was standing by a window of his office in the administrative building, located closer to the main palace, admiring a shrub with pale pink flowers and a sweet fragrance. As he heard the news, all thoughts of nature and beauty fled from his mind. Feeling dizzy, he quickly sat down on the nearest sofa. He suffered from hypertension and heart problems—the last thing he needed was a theft on his watch. 'H…how did this happen? When did you come to know?' Bilal asked, his voice shaking.

As Kalam explained the incident in detail, Bilal quickly took a pill from his pocket and placed it under his tongue. His mind was in turmoil. *What will I tell the trustees? How will they take the news? Will I be blamed?* Bilal thought nervously.

Finally, after Kalam had finished speaking, Bilal said, 'I'll come over immediately. Don't do anything till then. And don't let the two visitors get away.'

He called the senior-most trustee of the museum, Rehana Begum. A wise and experienced woman, she managed to not lose her cool after hearing the horrifying news.

'What has happened, has happened. Don't panic. I'll come over immediately. I'll see what needs to be done after assessing the situation myself,' she told Bilal. Rehana Begum's words helped Bilal calm down a bit. 'Yes, ma'am, please come down as soon as you can. I'll meet you at the museum. I'm going over there right now,' Bilal responded.

Rehana reached the museum within half an hour. Farhan rushed to Rehana as soon as she arrived and said, 'Ma'am, I'm so sorry that this has happened. I have no idea who did this, I swear,' he said, shaking and crying.

'Why are you crying, Farhan? Has anybody blamed you? No, na? Then why are you crying?' Rehana comforted him.

Bilal, who had met Rehana at the entrance and had come up with her to the third hall, where the theft had taken place, nodded. 'I'm sure that this is the work of some outsider,' Rehana reassured Farhan.

With his shaking hands folded, Farhan said in a slightly more composed manner, 'You're kind, ma'am, for believing me.'

'You have been an attendant here for over 16 years now. I trust you. Now go, wash your face and calm down. This is not the time to cry,' Rehana commanded.

Farhan wiped his eyes and obediently went and sat at his desk in the corridor of the museum after washing his face, feeling slightly better. He realized that Rehana was kind and would support him.

Together, Kalam, Rehana and Bilal inspected the unit from which the items had been stolen. They were shocked to see that the grille of the ventilator immediately above the cupboard had been unscrewed and removed. The thief must have entered from there. The CCTV camera placed directly under the ventilator was turned towards the wall, suggesting that the thief may have kicked it. There were long marks on the wall near the ventilator.

'These look like rope marks,' Rehana Begum said, inspecting the marks.

'Yes, I think so too. The thief must have used a rope to climb down from the ventilator,' Bilal added.

Rehana looked around. There were other items there, like a gold dagger and a gold handwritten Quran, which were probably more expensive and of greater historical value than the stolen artefacts. 'I wonder why these were not taken,' she mused.

Kalam shrugged. He had no idea. Right now, the only thing on his mind was whether the police would consider this to be an inside job and whether the museum staff, including himself, would become suspects in their eyes.

Rehana looked at Kalam and said, 'Okay, let me call the police from your office.'

Together, they went to Kalam's office and dialled the number of the Mir Chowk Police Station (PS). A few minutes later, there was no response.

'Maybe they are not in the station because of Janmashtami,' she guessed. She then decided to call Prince Muffakham Jah to give him the bad news.

The Prince was at his palatial Kensington Palace Gardens home, playing with his grandson, when he received Rehana's call.

'*Ya Allah*, what is it I am hearing! Who has done it? Have the police been called?' the Prince asked.

'Your Highness, I tried to call the police, but they are not responding,' Rehana responded.

'Okay, I have the Commissioner's number. I'll call him directly. In the meantime, you start sending e-mails to all the police stations.'

'Your Highness—'

'Yes, what is it, Rehana?' the Prince asked impatiently.

'Your Highness, the staff are all very worried. They seek your forgiveness that they couldn't prevent the crime. They are also apprehensive that the police might think that they stole the items.'

The Prince's tone softened immediately. 'Tell the staff that I trust them implicitly and they need not worry. I'll say the same thing to the police. Now, let me call the Commissioner. Then I'll call you back.'

Rehana noted the e-mail IDs of various police stations and started writing to them. Once she was done, she said a small prayer in her mind, wishing for the stolen items to be recovered.

∽

Around 11.00 a.m., the Assistant Commissioner of Police (ACP) Venkatesh Naidu, of Mir Chowk Station, was at home when his cell phone rang. It was Janmashtami, a public holiday, and he had been planning to go to the station in the afternoon. He took the call, a tad irritated.

It was a constable posted at his police station. 'Sir, I heard that there has been a theft in The Nizam's Museum.'

'What!? Who told you? Where are you?' ACP Naidu demanded.

'Rizvi—the head of private security at the museum—told me. I'm doing my rounds, Sir.'

'Why did he call you? Why haven't they filed an official complaint?'

'He said that they tried to call the police station, but nobody answered the phone. He said that they have sent an e-mail.'

'Hmm, there was a political rally yesterday, so many policemen from my team are on leave. Let me check the e-mail.'

After checking the e-mail, ACP Naidu urgently called for a police patrol car. This was a big incident. He would need to be on his toes for this job. As he waited for the patrol car to pick him up, he called his trusted officers, asking them to report to the museum immediately. As he got ready, he informed his wife, 'There has been a theft in the museum. I'll need to go and check immediately.' Waiting for the patrol car to arrive, the ACP called the museum. Kalam answered the phone. He confirmed that a theft had indeed taken place.

'I hope that you have closed the museum and detained the visitors who were inside when the theft was discovered?' ACP Naidu asked.

The curator responded in the affirmative.

'Good,' the ACP said. 'How many visitors are inside?'

'It's a Monday. Only two visitors came to the museum. They seem to be young students. One of them is a popular YouTuber. He says he was shooting for his next video. His girlfriend was his cameraperson. I don't think they stole anything. I've already asked my security head to detain and frisk them.'

'Okay, I'm coming immediately. In the meantime, please

prepare a list of all the employees, including those who resigned or were fired recently.'

The patrol car dropped the ACP at the museum. Many of his team members had also arrived by that time while others were on the way. Every entry and exit was sealed after the police entered the premises. The two detained visitors were told to wait. The police would interview them soon. The dog squad also came in. They swiftly sniffed the crime scene and once they were taken to the terrace from where the thief entered, they eagerly traced the path to the next terrace. However, they lost the scent after that. The dogs were then taken to the nearby lanes and bylanes but they couldn't find anything. The crime scene, which was the third of the adjoining rooms in the museum, was checked and cordoned off with yellow tape. After confirming all the details of the theft in person, the ACP called the Commissioner.

∽

Anjani Kumar, the commissioner of Hyderabad Police, was in his office when his phone rang.

'It's a call from London, Sir. Prince Muffakham Jah of Hyderabad is calling,' his personal assistant (PA) informed him in an awestruck voice.

While the call was being transferred, the Commissioner took a deep breath. *Why was the Prince calling him?*

Before he could ponder more, the Prince's refined voice reached his ears. 'Good morning Anjani Kumar saab, I hope I'm not disturbing you. I had to call, as it's an emergency.'

The Commissioner was acquainted with the Prince, as he had met the latter at various government programmes. He liked and admired the aristocrat. 'It's no trouble at all. Tell me, Your Highness, how may I help you?' he asked.

'There has been a theft in the museum at Purani Haveli. My estate manager and a senior trustee called me a few minutes back. More than the personal loss, I am disturbed by the loss of our heritage. I request you to please take up this case on priority.'

'What!? May I ask what was stolen?'

'As far as I know, a tiffin box studded with diamonds and a gold cup, saucer and spoon studded with an emerald and rubies.' The Prince's shock, bewilderment and hurt were reflected in his voice.

'Oh my God. Don't you worry, Your Highness. I assure you, we will nab the thief and recover the stolen artefacts at all costs.'

'I'm in London right now. Do I need to come down for this?'

'That won't be necessary as of now. I'll let you know if we need you to come down.'

'Thanks. In the meantime, my estate manager will ensure that everybody in the museum cooperates with you.'

'Thank you, Your Highness. I'll get on the job immediately.'

'This is my mobile number. Please feel free to call me at any time, day or night, if you need any help.' The Prince's suave manner and composure impressed the Commissioner.

'Yes, Your Highness. I'll look into this immediately.'

As soon as the call ended, the Commissioner received another call. It was ACP Naidu.

'Yes, I'm aware of the theft,' the Commissioner said, 'I'll come there as soon as possible. There must be CCTV cameras. Have you checked the footage?'

'Not yet, Sir. The museum's CCTV technician is on leave. We have sent a person to escort him here from his home,' ACP Naidu responded.

'Where is his home?'

'Nearby, Sir, in Mehdipatnam.'

'Okay, good. What about the list of current and former employees?'

'I am working with the curator on this. The list will be ready by the time you come here, Sir. I've also ensured that the visitors who were inside when the theft was discovered have been detained and the museum has been closed for the day.'

'Good job, ACP Naidu. Maybe you can also start searching and interviewing the visitors now.'

'Will do, Sir!'

The Commissioner then asked his PA, Haleem, to call the airport security team and ask them to remain alert, along with alerting the security teams of all major railway stations. Haleem also got in touch with the members of the Commissioner's Task Force, who directly reported to the Commissioner, and asked them to proceed immediately to The Nizam's Museum.

During the early 1980s, there had been rising cases of rowdyism, mafia rings and communal tensions within the city. To contain these, a specialized force had been formed in 1981 to help the commissioner of police maintain peace. This force was reconstituted as the Commissioner's Task Force in 1985.

In current times, the task force essentially consists of star performers in the police cadre. The task force is a well-developed institution that has been safeguarding Hyderabadis from all criminal elements—mafia, gangsters and other notorious criminals. Needless to say, by now, the very name 'task force' sends chills down the spines of all wrongdoers in the city.

It specializes in conducting raids and has the professional competence to apprehend criminals involved in serious offences. It is also deployed to investigate important crimes, like murders, dacoities, robberies, extortion, kidnappings, land grabbing and other organized crimes. The task force has an excellent track record of curbing rowdyism in Hyderabad. It pays special attention to maintaining communal harmony. The task force also plays a crucial role in handling all sensational and critical law-and-order issues.

As the Commissioner drove to the museum, he began to think about his plan of action. The theft of the Nizam's rich heritage hurt him personally. In this respect, he empathized with the Prince who, he knew, had been shocked and deeply saddened at the loss of the heritage items. He was also aware that there would be a public outcry once the newspapers and television channels got a whiff of the news of the theft.

The Commissioner had solved many sensational cases before. However, for some reason, he strongly felt that this theft from The Nizam's Museum was going to be particularly difficult to solve. On his smartphone, he googled similar museum thefts in other parts of the world. He was surprised to find that most museum theft cases had remained unsolved despite the involvement of heavyweight investigative agencies like the Federal Bureau of Investigation (FBI).

He went to the FBI website and was surprised to read the following details about the list of important unsolved museum heists:

- 7,000–10,000 looted and stolen Iraqi artefacts, 2003
- 12 paintings from the Isabella Stewart Gardner Museum, 1990

- 2 Renoirs and 1 Rembrandt stolen from Sweden's National Museum, 2000 (Recovered)
- Munch's "The Scream" and "The Madonna" from the Munch Museum in Oslo, 2004
- Benevenuto Cellini's Salt Cellar from Vienna's Kunsthistorisches Museum, 2003
- Caravaggio's "Nativity with San Lorenzo and San Francesco" from Palermo, 1969
- Davidoff-Morini Stradivarius violin from a New York apartment, 1995
- Two Van Gogh paintings from Amsterdam's Vincent Van Gogh Museum, 2002
- Cezanne's "View of Auvers-sur-Oise" from Oxford's Ashmolean Museum, 1999
- Da Vinci's "Madonna of the Yarnwinder" from Scotland's Drumlanrig Castle, 2003[4]

Anjani Kumar googled the most prominent among these: The Gardner Museum theft case. The museum was created by Isabella Stewart Gardner, a wealthy Boston arts patron who had amassed a world-class collection of paintings, sculptures, Asian and European antiquities and curiosities, like letters from Napoleon and Beethoven's death mask. In 1903, she arranged her 2,500-plus treasures inside a newly made Venetian-style palazzo that became her home as well as a museum open to the public.

Some time around midnight, on 18 March 1990, as St Patrick's Day festivities from the day before were winding down, her edifice was broken. Two thieves disguised as Boston

[4]"FBI Announces Top Ten Art Crimes', 15 November 2015, https://bit.ly/3Uoc8v8. Accessed on 21 September 2022.

police officers persuaded a guard to let them in to investigate a 'disturbance'. They, then, handcuffed the guard and another watchman in the basement, taped their wrists and mouths and for 81 minutes, brazenly and clumsily cut two Rembrandts from their frames, smashed glass cases holding other works and made off with a valuable, yet odd, haul. It included a Rembrandt, Johannes Vermeer's *The Concert*, Édouard Manet's *Chez Tortoni*, Edgar Degas' sketches, a bronze-plated eagle and a Shang-dynasty vase secured to a table by a bulky metal device that had probably taken them 10 minutes to pry apart. Left behind were prizes like a Titian, some Sargents, Raphaels, Whistlers and, inches away from Degas' works, a pietà sketch by Michelangelo.

Anyone who expected the art to quickly show up in the black market or to be used for some kind of ransom was disappointed. After the theft, the museum announced a reward of $1 million to anybody who could provide information about the thieves. But there was dead silence. Seven years later, the museum raised its reward to $5 million, again to no avail. A quarter-century later, empty frames still mark the spots where *The Storm* and other works had once been on display. Most of these masterpieces were never recovered.

From his preliminary research, Anjani Kumar realized that, in the past hundred years, worldwide, only about one per cent of museum theft cases have been solved and precious artefacts recovered. He began to feel nervous. What had he gotten into? If the mighty FBI couldn't solve such high-profile thefts, would he be able to solve this case? Who might be involved in the theft at The Nizam's Museum? Was it possible that an international gang of criminals was involved? Should he talk to Interpol? The thieves had probably had enough time to smuggle the artefacts out of Hyderabad by now. For all anyone knew, the objects could be carefully hidden in the baggage of an international smuggler travelling first-class to Dubai at this very moment. He had ensured that the airports and railway stations were alerted, but was that enough?

To allay his apprehensions, he turned his attention to museum theft cases that had been solved, the most famous of them being the Louvre Museum theft case. He quickly read up on the details of the case. He was surprised to find that this famous theft had been the handiwork of a single person, a worker at the museum. The museum's security had been lax enough for the culprit to simply walk off with the painting. This case gave him some hope. Maybe, the theft at The Nizam's Museum was also the job of some petty criminal or an insider. Then, it would be relatively easier to solve.

As he looked up from his phone, he saw that he was being driven into the small lane that ended at The Nizam's Museum. He took a deep breath to compose himself. He would decide on the next course of action after examining the crime scene.

3

THE INVESTIGATION STARTS

By noon, within an hour of the theft being reported, Anjani Kumar arrived at the museum with at least 20 police officers, where they met Rehana Begum, Bilal, Rizvi and Kalam. Rizvi had worked with the Hyderabad Police until his retirement and was now working for the private security company hired by The Nizam's Museum. He saluted the Commissioner and introduced himself. Rizvi also knew some members of the Commissioner's team and was comfortable working with them. The police, too, felt comfortable with Rizvi, as he had been one of their own.

'First, let us visit the scene of the crime. Then, I'll discuss this matter with you in greater detail,' Anjani Kumar told the team.

'Ma'am, you sit here and wait for me,' the Commissioner, always a thorough gentleman, said to Rehana Begum courteously. 'Bilal saab, you, along with Rizvi and Kalam saab, can please come with me,' he added.

Rehana Begum intervened, 'Bilal saab suffers from hypertension and has been feeling dizzy and nauseous since he received the news of the theft. He needs to visit a doctor.'

'No problem, Ma'am. Let him wait here. I'll instruct my team to interrogate him and let him go as soon as possible,' the Commissioner responded. Then, he turned to one of the ACPs accompanying him and said, 'Can you take care of this? Also, what about the visitors who discovered the theft? Are they being questioned?'

'Yes, Sir. ACP Naidu is already questioning them. He'll update us soon,' replied ACP Srinivas, a member of the task force. He was the one who usually coordinated with ACP Naidu of the Mir Chowk PS. The Commissioner and his team from the task force as well as some policemen from the Mir Chowk PS, along with Rizvi and Kalam, walked down the long corridor and entered the hall from where the precious artefacts had been stolen.

As they walked towards the empty showcase, Kalam said, 'Sir, thanks for coming down so promptly.'

The Commissioner nodded and said, 'I'm only doing my job. Now, tell me, when and how was the theft discovered?'

'Sir, as you can see, the display unit is in a corner and not easily visible from the entrance. So, our guards didn't notice anything unusual.'

'When does the cleaning of the museum take place?'

'Twice a day, Sir. Once in the morning before the museum opens and again in the evening after the visitors leave.'

'Then why was the theft not discovered today morning? Where's the attendant?'

The attendant Farhan was summoned.

Farhan folded his hand and howled, 'Commissioner sir, when I opened the hall, everything was in place. I don't think the items were missing at that time. I haven't stolen anything. I've worked in the museum for 16 years and not a single thing has ever gone missing. Ask Kalam saab if you don't believe me.'

'Calm down, calm down, nobody has accused you yet,' the Commissioner said kindly.

'But you're going to interrogate me, isn't it, Sir?' Farhan asked.

'Yes, it's part of the investigation. We will all be interrogated. Now, pull yourself together!' Kalam said impatiently. Farhan retreated, wiping his tear-streaked face with a rather dirty handkerchief.

ACP Chaitanya Kumar, who was accompanying the Commissioner, said, 'Maybe the thieves were aware of the KCR rally[5] and knew that the police would be focussed elsewhere.'

'Well, if the thieves have indeed thought about that, they are unusually smart fellows,' the Commissioner agreed and asked, 'How was the theft discovered?'

'Sir, a YouTuber and his lady friend were recording a video about The Nizam's Museum. They discovered the theft,' Kalam responded.

'When do you think the theft occurred?' the Commissioner probed further.

'On Saturday, after 5.00 p.m., once the visitors left, we cleaned up the museum. The theft couldn't have happened before that. On Sunday, the museum was closed for Janmashtami. Today morning, the theft was discovered. Farhan cleans the museum first thing in the morning. He didn't notice anything unusual. Then, these students came and raised an alarm,' Kalam responded.

---

[5] Janyala, Sreenivas, 'TRS Mega Rally Highlights: Confident of Forming Federal Front Without BJP, Congress, Says KCR's Son', *The Indian Express*, 2 September 2018, https://bit.ly/3Lt0efz. Accessed on 20 September 2022.

'That means the theft happened sometime after the museum opened today morning,' the Commissioner concluded.

'That must be the case, Sir,' the curator agreed.

'I thought that today, 3 September, is Janmashtami,' the Commissioner frowned.

'Sir, this time, Janmashtami fell on 2 and 3 September. The administrators had decided to give us our leave on 2 September,' Kalam responded.

'Maybe these students were somehow involved in the theft and wanted to be the first ones to upload the video of the crime scene,' Rizvi suggested.

'Hmm…I doubt that anybody would be so brazen. Where are these visitors?' the Commissioner asked Kalam.

'They are currently in a room close to my office, being interrogated by someone from your team. Would you like to talk to them?' Kalam asked.

'Yes, of course, I'll speak to them soon,' the Commissioner said as he reached the display unit where the stolen artefacts had been kept. The glass casing was intact. The lock was broken and Anjani Kumar could see the marks from the tools used to break open the lock of the showcase. There were also marks on the shelf where the artefacts had been displayed. The placard describing the history and details of the stolen artefacts was the only thing that remained—a silent testament to the despicable crime.

There were other magnificent gold and silver items displayed in the same area. It was an awe-inspiring sight for the entire police team. The Commissioner was particularly mesmerized by a gold throne on which the last Nizam used to sit. The rather musty smell of the museum, along with the high ceilings, the rough stone floors and lime-washed walls, momentarily transported Anjani Kumar back to the Nizam's era. But, he quickly returned to the difficult task at hand— identifying the thief and getting the precious antiques back.

Initially, the news of the theft had left the Commissioner numb with shock. However, now, looking at the empty display unit, the enormity of the crime hit him. The callous and insensitive thieves had shown no regard for the heritage of Hyderabad. For them, the artefacts had only been pieces of gold that they could sell to earn some money. He was filled with cold anger. *How dare they?* He forced himself to remain calm and composed. Anger would only cloud his judgement. He swore to find the robbers and bring the heritage items back to where they belonged. He would get justice for the people of Hyderabad. He looked around the hall. Everything else appeared to be intact. Still, to be sure, he asked Kalam, 'Have you checked if anything else has been stolen?'

'That is the first thing I checked, Sir. We are lucky in the sense that they only took four items: the tiffin box, cup, saucer and gold spoon.'

'Do you have any idea why they took only these items? Do they have any special significance? Any special historical value?'

'No, Sir. In fact, there are other items here that have a lot more historical significance,' the curator responded.

While the Commissioner was looking around, Rizvi pointed to the broken ventilator nearby. 'This is the ventilator through which the thieves must have entered. Look at the camera. They must have tried to damage it with their feet while sliding down the ventilator, but it is still working.'

'Did you get any footage of the thief?' Anjani Kumar asked.

'Unfortunately, no, Sir. As you can see, he was able to twist the bracket holding the camera. It will only show the footage of the blank wall,' Kalam answered.

'Still, I would like to see the CCTV footage from this camera. Maybe it has recorded something. Chaitanya, please send a constable to coordinate with the technician,' the Commissioner instructed.

The curator took out his cell phone and called the CCTV technician while a constable from the police team was dispatched to coordinate with him.

'Sir, I feel that this might be the work of some petty criminals rather than a sophisticated gang. They seem to have had little understanding of the historical value of the items on display. Only four somewhat historically insignificant items have been stolen, when the Holy Quran here, for example, would have had a lot more antique value,' ACP Chaitanya said to the Commissioner in a hushed tone.

'Yes, good point, Chaitanya, I hope so too. Petty criminals would be far easier to catch, but we need to be sure,' Anjani Kumar said, looking up at the ventilator. 'They must have used a rope to climb down from the ventilator. It's quite high up.'

'Look, Sir! There are fresh marks on the wall,' Inspector Madhu pointed at the marks.

Anjani Kumar carefully observed the ventilator from where he was standing. He looked at Madhu and said, 'Get somebody to measure the height of the ceiling and the ventilator from the floor. Clearly, they used a rope, as there is a rope mark on the wall border near the ventilator as well.' Then, another thought struck him. 'There are so many ventilators! How did the thieves know that they should come down this particular ventilator?' The Commissioner turned to Kalam, who had finished speaking to the technician by this time, and asked,

'Where is this ventilator fitted, Kalam saab? Can I go and see it?'

'Sir, that won't be so easy. To reach the terrace where the ventilators are installed, you will have to go up a broken wood staircase. It will be risky to climb it. Why don't you try to get up to the terrace using another metal staircase that is accessible from the next building?' Kalam suggested.

'No, no, Kalam saab. Don't worry. I will be able to scale it easily. Just get a rope for me,' the Commissioner responded.

Once the rope had been procured, the Commissioner carefully climbed up the rickety staircase and reached the terrace. Slowly, his team members followed. Rizvi also clambered up after them. Kalam, however, was too old and unfit to accompany the group.

'Kalam saab, you wait for me in your office. I'll join you shortly,' the Commissioner called down to him, adding, 'also, get a temporary room ready where I can hold meetings and my team can conduct interviews. All the staff members will be interviewed by my team.'

As soon as he reached the terrace, the Commissioner saw that there were many private buildings abutting the museum building. 'Oh my God, this is shocking, Rizvi saab! These buildings are not only damaging this heritage structure but also pose a threat to the safety and security of the museum. Anybody can enter the premises from the terraces of the adjacent buildings.'

The ventilators on the terrace, one of which was broken by the thieves to enter the museum

Source: The Hyderabad Police

'There is nothing we can do about it, Commissioner sir. These are the houses of private individuals. The Nizam's palace administration has been fighting cases with these individuals, since these are illegal encroachments. The mandatory 10 feet distance between buildings has not been maintained. However, the government is reluctant to enforce the rules because this is a predominantly Muslim area, I guess,' Rizvi explained, his frustration clearly visible on his face.

ACP Chaitanya, Inspector Madhu and other members of the task force had climbed up the rickety staircase and caught up with the Commissioner by the time he reached the broken ventilator. Anjani Kumar noticed rope marks on the parapet wall. 'Look at these marks, Chaitanya. Somebody tied a rope to this pillar and lowered the rope through the ventilator after cutting the grille open.'

'Yes, Sir. We are lucky it had been raining. The rope marks wouldn't have been so visible if it had been dry,' ACP Chaitanya responded.

'Yes, true. But look at the level of planning done by these thieves. They knew that they would need a long, thick rope, they knew how to reach this ventilator and they brought a chisel to cut open the grille. I am guessing the criminals are locals from this area. But, the question is: there are so many ventilators, how did they know that this was the ventilator closest to the artefacts they wanted?' Anjani Kumar wondered aloud. He increasingly suspected that the theft could have been an insider job. However, he decided to keep an open mind. While examining the nearby walls, suddenly, his keen eyes noticed an arrow drawn on the wall immediately above the broken ventilator. 'Who made this arrow, Rizvi? Had it been here since before the theft?' he asked.

Puzzled, Rizvi scratched his head. 'This is the first time I am noticing it. I'll ask my men if they know who did this.' As Rizvi walked away to phone his team members to find out more about the arrow, the Commissioner, along with the rest of the team, scrutinized the arrow. The Commissioner thought that this case had a striking similarity with the Louvre Museum case, where the *Mona Lisa* had been stolen in broad daylight. An ordinary carpenter, who had come to the Louvre for some repair work, had committed the theft. What if something similar had happened here as well? Maybe some mason had come to repair something, seen the expensive items and decided to steal them.

While Rizvi was away, ACP Chaitanya asked, 'What was the purpose of making the arrow mark?'

'That is obvious,' the Commissioner responded a bit

impatiently. 'With so many identical ventilators, they needed to know which ventilator they should cut open to enter. The question is: how did they know that this ventilator was closest to the display unit containing the artefacts they wanted to steal?'

'Yes, Sir. Maybe they selected it because they knew that there was a camera fitted near this ventilator. So, while coming in, they would be able to disable or damage it. The other reason could be that they knew exactly what they wanted to steal.'

'That means they either researched really well before the theft or it is an inside job.'

'Are such petty criminals capable of so much research?'

'Exactly, Chaitanya! It looks like some intelligent person was guiding them. This, again, leads to the insider angle.'

'But, Sir, since the curator said that there was no special historical significance to the stolen artefacts, I would guess that the thieves selected these items randomly. An insider would definitely know which the most expensive and historically significant artefact was and would steal that.'

'Yes. What you are saying makes sense. In that case, we will have to concede that the criminals did a recce of the area well. And this arrow that they made shows masonry expertise. Only an expert mason will be able to draw this neat an arrow on a concrete wall. I would say that the thieves are uneducated but intelligent, and are expert masons. Just ensure that the forensic team or the clues team thoroughly dusts the area and gets all possible fingerprints—especially in the area where they cut open the ventilator.'

'Yes, Sir.' Chaitanya nodded, making notes.

'As far as I can see, there are no footprints, but ensure that the clues team checks for that as well.'

Chaitanya added this to his notes while the Commissioner thought some more.

'Look, let's not rule out the insider angle. Let's look into the backgrounds of both Kalam and Rizvi. See if they have monetary problems, etc. In fact, do that for all the employees of the museum. Check what time Kalam and Rizvi came into their offices, if they had any unusual visitors, etc.'

'Yes, Sir. I'll also look into ex-employees. Maybe this is the handiwork of one such disgruntled employee.'

'Or a current employee. Check out the list of current employees and question them thoroughly. Also, check if the museum keeps a log of visitors to the museum. Else, they must have CCTV footage of the visitors. If it's an outsider's job, the thieves must have done a recce of the area and visited the museum multiple times for it. Ask the clues team to monitor the CCTV footage thoroughly. Whoever did this either thoroughly researched the area or it is an insider who knows the layout of the place well,' the Commissioner thought aloud.

'I think that you are right, Sir,' ACP Chaitanya agreed.

Just as the Commissioner and ACP Chaitanya were concluding their discussion, Rizvi returned and said, 'Nobody at the museum knows anything about the arrow. There has also been no repair work or any other activity on this terrace recently.'

'Okay, Rizvi. You can wait in Kalam saab's office now. We'll get back to you,' the Commissioner said abruptly. If an insider was involved, he didn't want any of the museum staff to be aware of what the police were thinking or doing. ACP Chaitanya nodded his approval.

The arrow made by the thief to mark the ventilator they would break to enter the museum (photo taken after the ventilator was repaired).

Source: The Hyderabad Police

When Rizvi left, the Commissioner continued, 'That arrow has been made by the thief so that he would know which ventilator to enter through. As Rizvi said, no repair work has been done recently. I guess that the thief has some degree of expertise in construction work. This is the kind of arrow construction workers typically draw during centring. I have seen these kind of arrows at construction sites close to my home. Only a construction worker could draw a neat arrow like this.'

'I agree,' Chaitanya Kumar nodded.

'Chaitanya, please note this point and collect the details of all masons in the vicinity and see if there are any property offenders[6] who are also professional masons,' the Commissioner instructed.

---

[6]Property offenders are people who have committed 'property crimes', which is a broad phrase that includes robbery, burglary and theft.

'Yes, Sir,' Chaitanya said, writing furiously in his notebook.

Anjani Kumar looked up and saw that there was another narrower terrace at a slightly elevated level over this terrace. He also noticed a short iron ladder that led to it. Followed by his team, he climbed the ladder and went to the terrace above. Manish, one of the sub-inspectors on the task force, pointed excitedly at another mark. 'Look, Sir, another arrow!'

'Yes…the thief obviously drew this as well. So, basically, he made his way through this terrace to the smaller terrace below. Then, from that terrace, he broke into the museum through the ventilator.'

'Yes!' Manish said animatedly.

'But how did he get onto this terrace?' Inspector Madhu asked. The answer was almost immediately obvious. At the end of the higher terrace was another small iron ladder.

The Commissioner turned to one of the constables, Mohsin, and said, 'Check what is on the other side of the wall. Why is an iron ladder situated there?'

Mohsin, a smart and athletic guy, quickly climbed the ladder. He looked down and shouted, 'This ladder is connected to another ladder on the other side, Sir. If I climb down that ladder, I will reach the terrace of the one-story building that houses the Mukarram Jah School.'

'Look carefully…can you see any footprints, fresh cigarette butts, pan masala packets, anything at all? Chaitanya, ask the clues team to look into this,' the Commissioner instructed.

'Yes, Sir…they are on the way,' Chaitanya informed.

'Well, call them again and ask them to hurry up,' the Commissioner said impatiently.

The ladder that the thieves used to move from the terrace of the museum to the terrace of the school building.

Source: The Hyderabad Police

'I can't see any footprint or pan masala packet, Sir,' Mohsin called out.

Anjani Kumar climbed the ladder to look for any such objects himself. The terrace was neat and well-kept. There were no used pan masala packets or any other such garbage.

Commissioner Anjani Kumar, ACP Chaitanya Kumar, Inspector Madhu and Sub-Inspector (SI) Anil looked on while Mohsin climbed down to the terrace of the neighbouring building. From there, he climbed up to another terrace slightly above the one he was on. Only a small parapet separated this terrace from the roof of the typical residential building next door. There was no gap between the two buildings, in clear violation of the Greater Hyderabad Municipal Corporation rules.

The ladder connecting the terrace of the museum to the terrace of the school building.

Source: The Hyderabad Police

'This could have been the route taken by the thief,' Anjani Kumar said.

As the Commissioner tried to follow Mohsin, the latter implored him to not climb the ladder. 'It's a bit rickety. You can reach this building by taking the lane next to the museum.'

'Yes, Sir, let's not risk climbing this ladder,' ACP Chaitanya agreed. He was worried that the Commissioner, in his determination to solve the crime at the earliest, would end up injuring himself.

The Commissioner acceded to his team's request, to their relief, and said, 'Okay Mohsin, wait there. We are reaching in a few minutes.' Taking Chaitanya, Anil and Madhu with him, he exited the museum and took the side lane to reach the private residential building.

Mohsin was leaning on the terrace wall, watching out for the Commissioner. 'This way, Sir,' he shouted as soon as he saw the Commissioner. The building was next to a masjid. There was a narrow staircase immediately next to the gate of the building, which led to the terrace on the second floor. There were some well-tended household plants, including a money plant, tulsi and aloe vera, in small pots along the staircase. As they reached the first floor, they saw the open door of a small apartment and heard a woman speaking to her kids. They went up another flight of stairs and reached the second floor, to the terrace. The Commissioner climbed the small wall separating this terrace from the museum building. *How easy it must have been to reach the museum! Such lax security!* He made a mental note to speak to the administrators of the museum regarding this.

After a thorough inspection, the Commissioner came out of the building along with his team. He saw a small, narrow lane about two metres wide. While a car couldn't possibly travel inside this lane, a bike could easily pass through. On the opposite side of the building was the white boundary wall of the masjid.

Mohsin squinted to look at the top of the mosque. 'There's a camera there,' he said, pointing to the roof of the mosque.

'That is good news indeed! Get the CCTV footage from them. This will help us analyse the entry and exit routes. Call the entire team here. We will try to see if we can get footage from more cameras if there are any,' Anjani Kumar said.

Mohsin, who had been born and brought up in the Old City and knew the area quite well, said, 'Yes, Sir. There are a few cameras in the area. There's one on top of that apartment building, two buildings after the masjid. There are some more along this small lane.'

'Okay! Chaitanya, ensure that all relevant CCTV footage is collected. Also, close all the lanes and by-lanes and visit every house to check if anybody has seen the thieves. I'll now go back and meet the curator,' the Commissioner instructed. When he returned to the museum, he met ACP Naidu. 'Did you question the blogger fellow?' the Commissioner asked.

'Vlogger, Sir. They seem to be harmless students. I doubt they were involved in the theft,' ACP Naidu responded.

'Okay, let's go and meet them.'

Gaurav and Pia were extremely nervous by this time. Based on the way ACP Naidu had questioned them, they were beginning to feel that they were the prime suspects in the case.

As soon as the police had left them alone after the first round of questioning, Pia had started bickering with Gaurav. 'You and your vlogging! Now, because of you, I am in big trouble. If the police file a criminal case against me, do you think I will ever get a US visa?'

'What! Are you planning to go abroad? You never told me!' Gaurav exclaimed furiously.

'Well, I was thinking about it. I would have told you about it when I decided. But now the opportunity of going abroad for a doctorate may never happen, thanks to your silly hobbies.'

'My silly hobbies? You, of all people, should not say such things. You know what a hit my YouTube videos are!'

'Huh! There are thousands of YouTubers like you! You

need to focus more on your education and career. I don't know how my parents will react if a criminal case is filed against me,' Pia began to sob.

'Pia, please don't cry,' Gaurav said, touching her arm.

'Don't touch me!' Pia exclaimed, flinching, just as the Commissioner walked in with ACP Naidu.

As soon as Gaurav saw the Commissioner, he said, 'Sir, we are students and vloggers. I have my own YouTube channel. We are not thieves, Sir. Please let us go.'

The Commissioner, a good judge of people, realized that ACP Naidu's assessment appeared to be correct. He looked at Gaurav and Pia and asked, 'Are you students?'

'Yes, Sir. My friend, Pia, and I are pursuing master's degrees from Osmania University. I earn a small amount of money through my YouTube channel. I regularly try to upload videos about Hyderabad. We are not thieves, Sir,' Gaurav explained. Pia was sitting quietly, trying to control her tears.

'Okay, Naidu, take their address and ID proofs and ask Inspector Madhu to talk to them once,' the Commissioner instructed as he turned to go to Kalam's office. The curator was waiting in his office with Rizvi, the CCTV technician and another constable, Hari, when the Commissioner walked in.

'Sir, Siyaam is in charge of the CCTV cameras. I'll leave you to question him,' Kalam said.

'Okay, let's take a look at the footage. Constable Hari, ask Inspector Madhu to join me,' the Commissioner said, dabbing his face with a handkerchief as he sat down. There was an old-fashioned fan whirring away from the high ceiling, but the day was hot and the fan was not quite up to the task of cooling the room. As soon as Inspector Madhu joined them, the Commissioner asked the technician to play the footage.

The Commissioner saw the thief coming down the rope attached to the ventilator. He was a lean, masked man of average height. The video was from a camera some distance away from the ventilator and the picture quality was rather grainy and poor.

'Sir, this is the footage from camera five, which was pointed towards the wall with the ventilator. It doesn't capture the display unit from which the thief took the gold box,' the technician commented.

In the footage, the thief seemed to kick the camera fixed to the wall below the ventilator.

'This is the ventilator over the display unit from which the thief stole the artefacts,' Siyaam explained to the Commissioner. After that, the footage captured the fully masked thief landing on the floor and letting go of the rope. Then, the thief moved out of the camera's range. It could capture only a few seconds' worth of footage.

'Show me the footage from the camera that the thief kicked away,' the Commissioner demanded.

The footage from that camera momentarily showed a dangling rope followed by a shaky picture of the hall and then a blank wall. The thief had cleverly managed to turn it away while he had been jumping down.

'Sir, as you can see in the footage from this camera, someone lowered a rope from above. Then, we can see a foot sliding down the rope and kicking the camera away, only recording the blank wall behind it. The other camera also captured the thief climbing down, but it was pointed at an angle away from the display unit. Hence, it only recorded the thief climbing down and up,' Siyaam explained.

So, the actual theft was not captured. Hmm...intelligent guy, the Commissioner thought. At least the footage had established that one of the thieves had entered the hall to commit the theft.

'What is the time in the footage?' the Commissioner asked.

'Sir, it was 3.25 a.m.,' Siyaam responded.

'So, the theft happened just before dawn today. That gives me some hope that the thief might not have had the time to smuggle the artefacts out of the country. Chaitanya, have you asked your men to check out the nearby railway stations and lodges?'

'Yes, Sir. ACP Naidu of the Mir Chowk PS is already taking care of that.'

'Now, wait a minute. The curator told me that Farhan hadn't noticed the theft when he cleaned up. Clearly, that cannot be the case if the theft took place after 3.25 a.m. He is lying. Inspector Madhu?'

'Yes, Sir. I'm planning to interrogate him. I'll find out, Sir,' Madhu responded.

'Fine, now let us check if a person with a similar build as the thief visited the museum in the past two days,' the Commissioner said, turning back to the technician, although he had a sinking feeling that this would not be of much help. The thief was of average build and height. So, even if he had visited the museum in the last two days, he wouldn't stand out among the crowd of visitors.

As he continued to view the footage from the past two days, Anjani Kumar started thinking about what his initial plan of action should be to recover the stolen items. He knew he would have to act fast, as there was a high probability of the precious artefacts being smuggled out of Hyderabad and possibly the country, which would make recovery next to impossible. He quickly analysed the strengths and capabilities of the teams working under his command—the Commissioner's Task Force, zonal crime team, clues team, IT team, etc. He mentally evaluated the tasks to be assigned to each team to crack the case. The Commissioner wanted to leave no stone unturned and was determined to utilize every resource available to him to its fullest potential. He nodded intently and, looking at Siyaam with his piercing stare, asked, 'Is it possible to see if any visitor resembling the thief came to the museum in the past few months?'

'Sir, we keep the CCTV footage for 31 days only.'

'Have you checked the footage for all 31 days?'

Siyaam scratched his head and, looking down to the floor, said in a low voice, 'No, Sir. I have only had the time to check for the last two days. I am sorry.'

'No need to apologize. Of course, these things take time. You do one thing—hand over all the available tapes. We'll look at them thoroughly.'

Turning to Inspector Madhu, the Commissioner immediately started instructing him, 'Take all the footage of the last 31 days from Siyaam and check it thoroughly. We have a few minutes of footage of the thief here. Check out all the visitors from the past 31 days and see if there is any match. The thief must have checked out the museum thoroughly before committing the crime. So, in all probability, they visited the museum several times. Check for repeat visitors and so on. You know the drill.'

He asked the task force to gather for a meeting. The room allocated to him near the curator's office was huge but had a musty odour, as it hadn't been used for some time. The ceiling had cemented beams and the green shuttered windows were large. Once they had been opened, a lot of light and air filtered into the room, reducing some of the mustiness. The floor was made of rough cement. The room had a huge, old-fashioned solid wood table and a few chairs. For a moment, the Commissioner was transported back to the world of the Nizams, but he quickly returned to the present.

Once the team had assembled in the room, the Commissioner said in his booming baritone, 'I'm sorry to have to disturb all of you, given that you have been working non-stop for the past three days for KCR's rally, but this is a serious issue. Heritage items have been stolen. These things are a matter of pride. We'll have to recover these artefacts at any cost.'

'We will recover them, Sir!' Chaitanya Kumar assured him enthusiastically, and the others nodded in agreement. The Commissioner's face glowed with pride. He had made no mistakes in putting his faith in his task force.

'We'll need to interview the museum staff to check if this was an insider job. However, let's not pressurize them right away. They are already nervous, so, even if they are innocent, they might be afraid of getting involved and clam up. I'll first address the entire museum staff and put them at ease. Even if one of them is involved in the theft, it won't be justified for us to intimidate all the employees. Each of them should be taken into confidence to build up the case and to collate the chronology of events leading up to the theft. They need to refresh their memories to recollect the events. So, ensure that they are calm when they answer your questions. Put them at ease before starting the interviews. Now, let's catch up and then, I'll ask the curator to assemble the museum staff so that I may address them,' the Commissioner continued.

After updating his team with his plans so that they had a

fair idea about all the details of the theft, the Commissioner addressed the museum staff. 'You will be interviewed by my team. As long as you are open and honest, you need not worry. The police do not wish to harass you but to find out what exactly happened. Remember, your support and cooperation are needed for us to recover the stolen items as soon as possible.'

Next, the Commissioner met Rehana Begum and Bilal. After assuring them that the police would leave no stone unturned to recover the stolen items, Anjani Kumar left the museum for his temporary camp office, located at the Old Commissioner's office. There, he had an emergency meeting with all wings of the city police. Some of the task force members, including Inspectors Madhu and Varma, stayed back to interview the museum staff and collect the CCTV footage. The clues team also stayed behind, dusting for fingerprints, taking photos of the crime scene and the entry and exit routes, which had been identified immediately, thanks to the Commissioner.

4

THE INTERROGATION

On Sunday, 2 September 2018, the Telangana Chief Minister, K. Chandrashekar Rao, addressed a massive rally, dubbed by the Telangana Rashtra Samithi (TRS), his party, as the biggest ever public meeting held in India. The Pragati Nivedana Sabha (meeting to report progress) held at Kongara Kalan on the outskirts of Hyderabad saw Rao speaking about the progress made in various sectors during the last four years. The rally was attended by 25 lakh people.[7] Speculation was rife about the possibility of early polls to the Telangana Legislative Assembly. The Hyderabad Police had a tough time controlling the crowds and their resources were strained severely. Everybody was tired.

Owing to this, the next day, on 3 September 2018, Inspector Madhu was unusually tired and sleeping soundly when his wife awakened him. He had switched off his mobile. So, his boss, ACP Chaitanya Kumar had called him on the landline.

---

[7]'Telangana CM KCR Presents his Govt's Progress Report at TRS Rally, No Announcement on Early Polls', *DNA*, 2 September 2018, https://bit.ly/3L5qNXI. Accessed on 12 September 2022.

'Madhu, you need to come to The Nizam's Museum as soon as possible. Huge theft in the museum. Big case,' Chaitanya had a habit of uttering, short, to-the-point sentences, particularly when talking to his subordinates.

'W...what happened, Sir?' Madhu stammered, a bit dazed and confused, as he had been fast asleep.

'The Nizam's antique artefacts have been stolen. A complaint has been lodged with the Mir Chowk PS by the administrator of the Nizam's estate.'

Inspector Madhu was jolted awake. 'Yes, of course, Sir. I'll be right there.'

He was part of the Commissoner's Task Force, South Zone. He quickly switched on his mobile and communicated with his team members to find out more about the issue. As he rushed to the bathroom, his wife, who had heard everything, said sharply, 'Don't leave without breakfast. I am preparing idlis for you.'

She knew that when work beckoned, Madhu often forgot to eat. In fact, every member of the Commissioner's Task Force was like him. For them, work was worship, as it was for the Commissioner.

For a moment, Madhu allowed himself the luxury of thanking his luck for his wife and how well she cared for him despite the fact that he spent most of his time at work. Then, he switched back to work mode. Today would be a busy day.

ᶜᵄ

Inspector Madhu sighed as he looked at the long list of employees he had been asked to interrogate. He was sitting in the teacher's chair in an empty classroom of the school that was located on the ground floor of the wing that housed The Nizam's Museum. It was going to be a hard day. Just a few hours ago, he had been fast asleep in bed with no inkling that the day would turn out like this.

The first name on his list was Farhan, the attendant in charge of the hall from where the artefacts had been stolen. He asked a constable to send for Farhan, who entered shaking in fear.

Inspector Madhu remembered the Commissioner's advice and decided to put Farhan at ease. He indicated for Farhan to sit down on the chair placed in front of him, on the other side of the teacher's desk.

'As-salaam Alaikum, Farhan. Have you had lunch yet?' Inspector Madhu began kindly.

'Walaikum As-salaam, yes, janaab,' Farhan said, relaxing slightly upon hearing the Inspector's kind tone.

'So, Farhan, how long have you worked in this museum?' Inspector Madhu asked, looking into his eyes.

'Sir, 16 years. My father also used to work as a khansama in the Nizam's Palace when the seventh Nizam was still ruling Hyderabad,' Farhan said more confidently.

'Oh ho! So have you been residing in this part of the city for a long time?' Madhu asked, raising his eyebrows.

'Yes, my father built a house here. I stay in the same house, Sir. We have been long-time residents of this area,' Farhan said with a proud smile.

'Do you remember the days of the Nizam's rule?' Madhu enquired with genuine interest, as he was a history buff.

'I don't personally remember, Sir. But, I have heard stories from my father about the seventh Nizam. In 1947, when India gained independence, he was considered the richest man in the world. My father used to tell us stories of his eccentric behaviour. He owned a 100-piece dinner set of solid gold, but he ate his frugal meals off a tin plate,' Farhan responded proudly. Clearly, he still thought of the days of the Nizam as the golden era.

'Really? That's interesting!' Madhu exclaimed.

'Yes, Sir. And he cut down his palaces' electricity consumption to save money. My father says that he had a huge diamond, which he considered unlucky and hid it in one of his shoes. It was found when his clothes were being auctioned.'

'Arre wah!'

'Yes, janaab,' Farhan continued with a smile, 'he wrapped diamonds in old newspapers and used them as paperweights. My father says that he even smoked cigarette butts left behind by visitors. Yet, his vaults contained a collection of the most precious jewels imaginable.'

Inspector Madhu judged that Farhan had become comfortable enough in his presence by now. Time to get down to business. 'Well, Farhan, these are all very interesting tales. But let us come back to the theft.'

Immediately Farhan stiffened defensively. But, he didn't clam up as much as he would have before. Instead, he said, 'Frankly, Sir, I have no idea who could have done this. I think that those two college students who came here today and were doing the video recording—those two must have taken the artefacts.'

'But Farhan, we have checked the CCTV footage. The theft happened around 4.00 a.m. today morning. You must have noticed the theft when you cleaned that area, right? Why didn't you inform anyone earlier?' Madhu asked, a little more curtly. Farhan started to shake, but he didn't respond.

'Come on Farhan, why didn't you inform anyone? Were you afraid that they would accuse you of the theft?'

'No, no, Sir. N…nothing of that sort, Sir. They all t…trust me.'

'Then why didn't you inform anybody?' Madhu demanded irritably.

'J…janaab,' Farhan gulped as he tried to speak.

'Tell me, Farhan,' the Inspector looked strictly at Farhan.

'J…janaab, I genuinely didn't notice the theft.'

'How come? Do you think I am a fool? I have been patient with you, Farhan. But now I am getting angry! Tell me why didn't you report the theft?' Madhu demanded, jerking his head questioningly and threateningly waving his forefinger at Farhan.

'J…janaab, *Allah kasam* I didn't notice because I didn't clean that area today,' Farhan confessed. Folding his shaking hands in front of the inspector, he continued, 'Please don't tell the management, Sir.'

'Why didn't you clean?'

'The maid didn't come today. So, I was supposed to sweep that area. But my legs were paining so I thought I won't sweep. Anyway, that area was quite clean,' Farhan added hastily.

'Are you telling the truth?' Madhu asked, staring Farhan down with a penetrating glare.

'Yes, Sir, *Allah kasam*. You can check the CCTV footage if you like,' Farhan said, clutching a tabeez tied around his neck with a black string.

'Okay,' Inspector Madhu said, making a mental note of verifying Farhan's tale with the footage. He was sure that Farhan was telling the truth, otherwise he wouldn't have been confident about his tale being verified against the footage. But again, if he had committed the theft, he would have wanted it to be discovered as late as possible by somebody else so the blame could fall on that person. In that case, he might have deliberately not swept the area and pretended that he had been in pain. Anyway, Madhu decided to let Farhan go, for now, saying, 'I believe you. But you must never lie to the police again. Understood?'

Farhan nodded.

'You may go now but make sure you remain in Hyderabad. Don't move out of town without informing us. We might call you again for questioning. Is that clear?'

Farhan nodded eagerly again, saluted and left the room, relief written large on his face.

The curator of the museum was the next person on Madhu's list. A constable brought Kalam to the interrogation room. He looked visibly nervous. Inspector Madhu wondered if it was a natural reaction in the presence of the police or if the man was guilty and was feeling nervous. Kalam was an elderly, scholarly looking man. Madhu didn't think the man was capable of committing the theft. Still, one never knows.

Again, he strove to put the curator at ease. 'Good afternoon, Sir. Nice to meet you,' he stood up and offered his hand. When Madhu shook Kalam's hand, he noted that the curator's hand was sweaty—another sign of nervousness. To put him at ease, the Inspector smiled kindly and said, 'How long have you worked here?'

'Inspector saab, I have worked here for four years,' Kalam responded. He had a thin, reedy voice, probably made thinner by his nervousness in front of the police.

Madhu smiled and said, 'Sir, I have always wanted to know:

what exactly is the role of a curator? I mean, what do you do?'

'Well, I curate!' Kalam responded with a smile, his eyes twinkling, despite his initial nervousness.

'And what exactly does that involve?'

'Well, I decide what artefacts should be displayed, how they should be cleaned—things like that. I maintain records of the various pieces that we have, including the pieces that are not on display. I also research these pieces to explain and justify their significance to the collection.'

'Was this museum started by the seventh Nizam?'

'Yes, this building was built by Mir Osman Ali Khan, the last Nizam of Hyderabad, to stock the gifts and mementoes presented to him when he completed 25 years of his rule in 1936. Later, it was converted into a museum so that the gifts could be displayed for visitors to see. Mir Osman Ali Khan was an erudite person, Saab. He was always interested in promoting education and science. Interestingly, Sir Ronald Ross made the landmark discovery that malaria was transmitted by mosquitoes and laid the foundation for its vaccination in Hyderabad. He received the Nobel Prize in Medicine for his research, which he conducted in the erstwhile Nizam's Hyderabad. It was known then as a medical hub in the subcontinent.'[8]

'Oh wow! I certainly did not know this. The Nizams were so advanced for their times. It's amazing.'

'Yes, it's a shame that his heritage is now going to the dogs like this,' the curator sighed.

Inspector Madhu paused, sympathizing with the curator.

[8]M. Somasekhar, 'Hyderabad's Ronald Ross: Remembered but also Forgotten', *Deccan Chronicle*, 13 May 2020, https://bit.ly/3qwBkBQ. Accessed on 12 September 2022.

Then, he said, 'Okay, I heard that you guys keep the CCTV footage for a maximum of 31 days and after that, you overwrite them with the new footage. Why do you maintain records for such a short duration?'

'Actually, Sir, we have a shortage of funds. The government does not fund us. We are privately funded by the trustees of the museum. So, money is scarce. In fact, when one of the cameras was not working, it took 10 days to get the money sanctioned to repair the camera. So, you can imagine our situation here,' Kalam confessed with a sigh.

After some more small talk, Madhu let the curator go. The next man on his list was Bilal, the estate administrator. The man had a thick beard and was borderline obese. He huffed and puffed into the room. He was sweating profusely.

Is he panting and sweating because he is nervous? Inspector Madhu wondered.

Bilal supplied the answer. 'Saab, I suffer from hypertension. Today's events have aggravated my problem. So, I had to take an extra dose of my medication. This medicine makes me sweat a lot.'

'Maybe you can shift the chair to sit under the fan,' Madhu suggested.

After Bilal shifted the chair and dabbed his face with a white handkerchief, Madhu said, 'Kalam saab was telling me that money for the maintenance of the museum is scarce. Why is that so?'

Bilal paused for a minute as if wondering what the correct response would be. Then, he said, 'I really don't know all the details, Inspector saab. But I'll tell you what I know. The relatives of the seventh Nawab who are still alive are all highly impoverished. Those who have escaped abroad are luckier, since it is far easier to maintain a facade there. The Cambridge-educated, 46-year-old grandson of the last Nizam, based out of Australia, and the official "guardian" of the Nizam's many trusts, Barkat Ali Khan, is one of them.

'The trusts, 50 in all, with total funds of about ₹110 crore, have been a major bone of contention between the surviving descendants. A large number of them accuse Barkat Ali of being indifferent to the affairs of the trusts. In fact, quite a few other trusts have already been dissolved due to ill-advised investments,' Bilal explained.

'Oh! But wasn't the seventh Nawab the world's richest man? How come the next generation became so poor?' Madhu probed further.

'Infighting among the existing relatives, taxes and poor investments,' Bilal sighed. 'The famed family jewels of the Nizam, kept in few of the trusts to ensure income for his offspring, have become matters of litigation and intense acrimony, with large portions of them being sold off to pay taxes,' Bilal added, shaking his head sorrowfully.

'How long have you worked here?' Inspector Madhu was surprised at the sorry state of affairs, but he didn't want to deviate from his investigations by enquiring more. Anyway, he felt that Bilal was now comfortable enough in his presence.

'Oh! Over 40 years now. In fact, I'm looking forward to my retirement. I only wish that this theft hadn't happened just before my retirement. Whatever few relics we have left of our rich heritage are being eyed by bad people. I wish the government would take over the maintenance of the museum. Only then would we have enough money to properly maintain this space. The museum and its artefacts are the only things that can be preserved as signs of our more prosperous times, but precious little is being done by the government. Anyway, as I said, I'm looking forward to my retirement and getting away from this mess, to be honest with you.'

'Right, Bilal saab. Thanks for your time. Please let us know if you go out of town. We might need to interview you again.'

'What? Again?' Bilal was aghast. 'Like I said before, I suffer from hypertension, Inspector sir. Such interviews really take a toll on my health.'

'We will try our best not to disturb you,' Inspector Madhu assured him. 'But still, please keep yourself available for the next month or so, in case we need to talk to you again.'

The next person on Madhu's list was Gaurav. But before interviewing the vlogger, he looked Gaurav up on his phone. Gaurav indeed was a YouTuber as he had claimed. Madhu quickly browsed through some of his videos. There was a vlog on Jummerat Bazaar, which he found particularly interesting. The videos were well-researched and he liked the happy-go-lucky demeanour of the man. He doubted that this young man was capable of committing a daring theft like this.

By the time they were interrogated, Gaurav and Pia were fed up with their seemingly endless wait. They were too tired and hungry to even bicker with each other. It was around 4.00 p.m. and all they had eaten was a meagre breakfast. They hadn't been allowed to go out for lunch by the constable guarding the room in which they had been detained.

Inspector Madhu asked the constable to get Gaurav and Pia. Gaurav was fuming. He was no longer nervous. As soon as he and Pia entered the classroom, he said in an incensed voice, 'Sir! What is this? I just discovered the theft. Why are you treating us like criminals? I should have walked away without reporting the theft. In this day and age, one should stop being a good citizen.'

'Calm down, calm down,' Inspector Madhu said soothingly. 'We don't really think you had anything to do with the actual crime. I was going through your YouTube channel. You have quite a lot of subscribers!'

Gaurav's anger dissolved at the praise coming from a senior police official. '193,000 subscribers, Sir!' the young man said, his face filling with pride. 'My videos get millions of views.'

'That's excellent. Now let's get down to business so that I can let you go as soon as possible,' Madhu said, flipping his notebook to a fresh page where he was jotting down salient points of each meeting.

Putting his pen down on the notebook, he looked up at Gaurav, smiled and said, 'Tell me, how did you discover the theft?'

For what seemed like the nth time that day, Gaurav described how he had discovered the theft. But he knew that getting angry or losing his patience would be counterproductive.

After Madhu finished taking notes, he said, 'That is all.'

Pia, who had been sitting quietly all this while, now said, 'Sir, I am planning to go abroad for further studies. Will you be filing criminal cases against us?'

She folded her hand in front of Madhu and said, 'Sir, I won't be able to get a visa.'

'Don't worry, Ma'am,' Madhu said, smiling at the nervous young woman. 'The police are neither insensitive nor illogical. We won't be filing any charges against you, unless, of course, there is solid evidence of your involvement. But, as of now, you needn't worry. You can leave now.'

'Thank you, Sir,' Pia said gratefully, smiling with relief.

As they came out of the museum, Gaurav looked sadly at Pia. He wondered whether a long-distance relationship would work between them if she moved abroad. *Pity, really, she is a good camerawoman*, he thought. Then, he cheered up. Maybe he, too, could move abroad and they could continue their vlogging from there. *Que sera sera*. But, right now, they would have lunch.

5

AT THE OLD CP CAMP[9]

When the Commissioner reached his temporary office, it was past 3.00 p.m. He was sweaty and tired, but there was no time to rest. He found that the mini-conference hall was packed with the people in charge of various wings, all waiting patiently for him to brief them. All of them were upset. The burglary of the heritage items was a source of major concern and a blow to their pride. There was not a single person in the hall who didn't want to catch the criminals and recover the antique items. Emotions were running high and everybody was eager to participate in the investigation. Anjani Kumar could resonate with the officers' emotions. However, he needed to calm them down first and make everyone understand the importance of working on the case with a cool and composed mind. He sat down in his air-conditioned office and sighed in relief.

His priority was ensuring that the thieves did not smuggle the stolen items out of Andhra Pradesh and Telangana, if

---

[9]Commissioner of Police Camp Office, which is located in the old city of Hyderabad.

possible. He conferenced with the commissioners and senior officers of Cyberabad, Rachakonda and other areas of Andhra Pradesh and Telangana, informing them of the theft and requesting help in setting up roadblocks and vehicle checks so that the thieves could be caught if they tried to cross the border.

'When did the theft occur?' one of the officers asked.

The Commissioner paused for a minute to consult the notes he had taken while inspecting the crime scene. Then, he said, 'We have CCTV footage of the thief climbing down from the ventilator of the museum around 3.25 a.m., give or take another hour for the actual theft. I would say, they must have escaped the museum with the booty at around 5.00 a.m.'

'It's after 3.00 p.m. now. It would have been better if you had informed us earlier.'

'I have just come back from the crime scene with the details. It was impossible for me to call earlier,' the Commissioner bristled at the implied criticism. But he quickly composed himself. Now was not the time to lose control. 'The thieves are extremely intelligent, in my opinion. They have left very little evidence at the crime scene. They must have anticipated that border security will be notched up by the police. I believe that they are in Hyderabad, lying low and waiting for the hullabaloo to be over before they try to smuggle out the items. So, all is not lost. They might try to smuggle out the items after things have cooled down a bit. If you guys stay alert, it would be helpful.'

Immediately after finishing this call, the Commissioner called a meeting with the local police and some members of the task force who had come back with him. The men had been waiting patiently for his update. All of them started speaking when he entered the conference hall. He held up his hand to stop them. Once there was total silence, he spoke, 'Now is not the time to let our emotions take over. We have to work calmly. We shouldn't let our emotions get the better of us, as that will be a recipe for failure. Now, will you help me recover the stolen items?'

'Yes, Sir!' the officers roared in unison.

The Commissioner updated the officers about what he had seen and learnt at the crime scene. He had full faith in his team and was sure that the stolen items would be recovered. Still, he added a word of caution, 'Museum thefts are very difficult, guys. Most such thefts have never been solved. The only known theft that has been solved was the theft of the *Mona Lisa* from the Louvre Museum in Paris in 1911.'

The Louvre Museum, Paris

Source: iStock

'Louvre what?' one of the inspectors asked.

'The Louvre Museum in Paris, France—it is the world's largest museum housing wonderful works of art by the world's greatest painters and sculptors, like Leonardo da Vinci, Pablo Picasso and so on. It is the number one tourist destination of Paris,' the Commissioner explained, fondly remembering his trip to the museum a few years back.

'Sir, has only one theft occurred in that museum so far?' one of the constables asked.

'Oh, no. The Louvre is no stranger to thefts. There have been many more thefts, but none were solved.[10] So, like I said, museum thefts are extremely difficult to solve. We'll need to put in our best effort to solve this case.'

'Sir, wouldn't such a place have top-notch security? Yet, it was burgled?' another inspector asked flabbergasted.

'Actually, the first theft happened in the early twentieth century. The security at that time had not been tight. But yes, after that theft, they improved the security. Though this theft happened some time back, it's important for us to understand the case, as I feel there is a lot of similarity between that case and ours. That theft was committed by an ordinary carpenter. No international gangs were involved.'

'Sir, do you mean to suggest that an international gang may not be involved here?' one of the officers, who had not been at the crime scene, asked, raising his eyebrows.

---

[10]On 3 March 2021, two pieces of ornate sixteenth-century armour were returned to the Louvre after a nearly four-decade absence. They had been stolen from the museum on 31 May 1983, only to be recovered 38 years later. But, in this case, the pieces were voluntarily returned thus, the police cannot be credited.

'That is my gut feeling from the preliminary investigations,' the Commissioner replied.

'What did the carpenter steal? And, more importantly, how could a common man like him know the value of that particular painting?' a team member asked in a bemused voice.

The Commissioner smiled at this comment. 'He stole Leonardo da Vinci's *Mona Lisa*[11], also known as *La Gioconda*. It is the most famous painting in the world. The carpenter knew about it, as he was originally from Italy and it's a very well-known painting there. The theft of this fabulous object in 1911 created a media sensation. The police were as baffled as everyone else. Pablo Picasso was a prominent suspect, but there was no evidence against him either.'[12]

'What! The world-renowned painter was also a suspect?' another inspector asked, looking at the Commissioner, eyes wide with amazement.

'Yes. Two years went by before the true culprit was discovered—an Italian petty criminal called Vincenzo Peruggia who had moved to Paris in 1908 and worked at the Louvre for some time. He went to the gallery in a white smock that all employees wore and hid until the museum closed for the night to remove the *Mona Lisa* from its frame. When the gallery reopened, he walked out unobtrusively with the painting under

---

[11] About the *Mona Lisa*: Innumerable efforts have been made over the years to identify who she was and explain what her enigmatic smile signifies, what she says about femininity, if anything, and why she has no eyebrows. When da Vinci was invited to France by Francis I in 1516, the former took the painting with him. The king bought it, and, after the French Revolution, it was placed in the Louvre. Napoleon took it away to hang in his bedroom, but it was later returned to the Louvre.

[12] McKenzie, Sheena, '*Mona Lisa*: The Theft that Created a Legend', CNN, 19 November 2013, https://cnn.it/2MsTcw5. Accessed on 22 August 2022.

his smock, attracting no attention, and took it to his lodgings in Paris,' Anjani Kumar explained.

'So, in that case, for two years, at least, the case remained unsolved? Then how was he caught?' the inspector asked, tapping his fingers on his chin.

'He was caught while trying to sell the piece. He hid the *Mona Lisa* in his lodgings in Paris for two years. It was not until December 1913 that Peruggia, assuming the name Leonardo Vincenzo, wrote to an art dealer in Florence, named Alfredo Geri, offering to bring the painting to Italy for a reward of 500,000 lire.[13] He travelled to Florence by train the following month, taking the *Mona Lisa* in a trunk, hidden beneath a false bottom. After checking into a hotel—'

'An ordinary hotel?' a team member interrupted the Commissioner.

'How does that matter?' the Commissioner asked waving his hand impatiently at this irrelevant question.

'No, I thought that now that that guy had some money, he would check into some swanky hotel. In that case, our criminals could also do something similar,' the team member said hastily to mollify the Commissioner.

'Well, no. It was just a third-rate hotel, like some of our lodges. So, I highly recommend that you guys check out some of the lodges in the Old City and ask your informer networks to keep their eyes and ears open.'

The men nodded eagerly. Assuaged by the inspector's explanation, the Commissioner sipped water from a glass and continued, 'Subsequently, the hotel where Peruggia stayed

---

[13]'...How *Mona Lisa* Was Finally Found', PBS, https://to.pbs.org/3pBKNHK. Accessed on 22 August 2022.

shrewdly changed its name to the Hotel La Gioconda. Anyway, after resting in the hotel, he took the painting to Geri's gallery. Geri persuaded him to leave it for expert examination and promptly informed the police. The police arrested Peruggia later that day. The great painting was duly returned to the Louvre and has hung there safely and enigmatically ever since.'

'Thank God for that,' an inspector said.

'Yes. But the reason I told you this story is that I am sure we can recover our stolen artefacts too. The thieves will try to sell them. Hopefully, they will do so within India. We should leverage our informer networks to see if they have seen or heard something. Do you guys agree?' the Commissioner asked, looking around at his team to gauge their reaction. All of them nodded approvingly.

'Yes, there are quite a few similarities between the theft of the *Mona Lisa* and the one in The Nizam's Museum. Like the Louvre Museum case, this theft too seems to be the handiwork of petty criminals who are more interested in making money than acting on any particular interest in art and culture. In both cases, security was lax and the perpetrator had very little difficulty in stealing the items. In the Louvre case, the thief was caught when he tried to sell the priceless artefact. So, there is a high probability that we too will be able to catch the thieves when they try to sell the artefacts,' ACP Chaitanya said.

'Yes,' the Commissioner said, nodding his head in agreement. There was a pause. Then, looking a bit glum, Anjani Kumar commented, 'I know that this will be an extremely challenging case. The thieves may try to smuggle the artefacts abroad as soon as possible. Alert the airport authorities again. Go and meet them personally. Revisit the crime scene. I'll need a report every day from all the teams that I'll be forming soon.'

As the team of policemen nodded, the Commissioner's face brightened again. 'There's hope. I was reading the FBI's opinions on museum thefts. According to them, criminals who steal high-value artworks tend to be better thieves than businessmen. They don't understand that the true art in a heist isn't stealing, it's selling. So, hopefully, we will be able to catch the thieves when they try to sell.'

'Yes, Sir. Also, thanks to the media attention on the case, every potential buyer will know that these are stolen artefacts,' a team member said encouragingly.

'Exactly! The people who can pay that kind of money aren't interested in owning something they could never sell and could possibly go to jail for possessing,' the Commissioner added, his eyes shining with hope.

'Yes, Sir, the thieves will have a tough time selling the artefacts now,' the team member agreed.

'Good!' the Commissioner rubbed his hands together. 'Again, I repeat, a cool and composed mind will be more productive. I'll bear the entire pressure of this case. So, you all please proceed without any pressure. But, remember, this is not just a routine case. It's a matter of our pride. We have to get these heritage items back at any cost.'

After this pep talk to boost the morale of the investigating officers, the Commissioner sat and reviewed the Mir Chowk PS staff's work, where the FIR for the theft had been lodged. By this time the task force members had come back and reported to the Commissioner. They were bursting to give their input.

'Sir, the thief climbed down a rope, right? This is how the rowdy sheeter Shaukat works. I am sure he committed this theft. I know him inside out. He is brazen enough to try such a high-profile burglary,' Inspector Chenna said, waving his forefinger confidently.

'Does Shaukat work as a part of a gang? This robbery couldn't have been committed by a single person,' the Commissioner said. He deliberately tried to find out if Shaukat worked as a part of a ring, trying to ascertain whether Chenna's premise was correct.

Chenna's face fell. He hadn't realized that this robbery was probably too big to have been handled by a single person. 'H…he used to be a lone operator before. Maybe he has joined a gang now. I'll try to find out,' he stammered a bit uncertainly.

'Does he have masonry experience?' the Commissioner probed further.

'Sir, I don't think so, but I'll enquire. Maybe somebody else in his gang has masonry experience,' Chenna said, embarrassed, wishing he had done some more research before opening his mouth.

'Yes, find out if he has a partner, or has joined some gang. Also, check the video footage of the thief climbing down the rope. See if you can identify him,' Anjani Kumar instructed.

'If the thief has masonry experience, I would say that Mir Mohammad may be our man. He works as a mason, but he has been involved in a burglary as well. However, he is a heavy-set man and I don't think he would be able to climb ropes,' Constable Krishna contributed eagerly, not to be outdone by Chenna.

'Good, you guys are thinking in the right direction,' the Commissioner smiled encouragingly and continued, 'as per the footage that I have seen, the thief is lean, young and agile. The arrows found at the crime scene indicate that he has masonry experience. But, whether he operated alone, I'm not sure. I'm forming a team to check out the CCTV footage from all the nearby areas for the entry and exit points of the criminals. If he has a partner, we will find out. In the meantime, as I said, keep your eyes and ears open.'

While the Commissioner was in the team meeting, many reporters called his PA asking for updates on the case. The PA, in turn, called Anjani Kumar, who checked the news quickly and saw that the theft was breaking news, both locally and nationally.

Just two days ago, on 1 September 2018, the Nizam's precious gold tiffin box, a gold cup and saucer, estimated at over ₹50 crores together, had been on display in their majestic setting. On 3 September, the artefacts were gone. News of the theft had spread like wildfire. Local television channels, like Sakshi TV and ETV Telugu, broadcast the footage of the front of the museum, with police personnel bustling around busily. One sub-inspector gave a short soundbite confirming the story of the theft.

The story headlined national newspapers and online publications, like *Hindustan Times*[14], *Firstpost*[15], *India Today*[16], *Deccan Chronicle*[17] and *The Economic Times*, over the next few weeks.

---

[14] Apparasu, Srinivasa Rao, 'Jewel-Studded Utensils Worth 50-Crore Stolen from Hyderabad's Nizam Museum', *Hindustan Times*, 4 September 2018, https://bit.ly/3py0EHp. Accessed on 22 August 2022.

[15] Indo-Asian News Service, 'History Robbed: Gold Tiffin Box, Diamond Studded Cup Stolen from Nizam's Museum in Hyderabad; Investigation Underway', *Firstpost*, 4 September 2018, https://bit.ly/3Cjr3A3. Accessed on 22 August 2022.

[16] Pandey, Ashish, 'Diamond-Studded Teacup, Gold Tiffin Box Stolen from Nizam Museum of Hyderabad', *India Today*, 3 September 2018, https://bit.ly/2Ndmyhy. Accessed on 21 September 2022.

[17] Suares, Coreena and Naveen Kumar, 'Nizam Museum Theft: Doubts Over Gold Cup Raised and Rested', *Deccan Chronicle*, 21 September 2018, https://bit.ly/3Sid4PQ. Accessed on 21 September 2022.

Some of the members of the task force and the clues team had stayed back at the museum after the Commissioner had left, and he wanted all the latest updates. He called to ask if all the members were available now. When the response was in the affirmative, the Commissioner decided to hold another meeting with all the members of the task force and clues team. The rumblings in his stomach reminded the Commissioner that he had forgotten to have lunch. He drank another glass of water to ease the discomfort and asked the constable guarding his office to invite the members of the two teams into his office immediately. He also asked the constable to bring in some more chairs to the office so that the team could sit comfortably. As he waited for the team to arrive, he called Haleem, his PA, to dictate a press release, assuring the public that the police were on the case and the investigation was underway, although it was too early to have any more updates. By the time he wrapped this up, the team had gathered outside his office. He called them inside. They came in and saluted him, as was the custom.

Once everyone had settled down, Anjani Kumar started the meeting by reiterating their importance to this case. 'As you know, you are the best of all my officers. The time has come for you to prove your mettle again. This is an important case and pressure will build up from all quarters. The government's top brass, politicians, the administrative machinery, media, both print and electronic, the general public and the museum authorities will all monitor the progress of this case. But, ignore all the hullabaloo and just focus on the work at hand. Remember, we might get negative press and receive a lot of flak if we can't solve this case quickly. Don't let any of these events distract or dishearten you. If we focus and do our jobs sincerely, we will ultimately win. We must ensure nothing is overlooked in investigating this case. All possible angles should be investigated with utmost sincerity.'

The task force team agreed enthusiastically. 'We will do our best, Sir,' they chorused. The Commissioner felt reassured by their response.

'This is a major challenge for the Commissionerate and it's my responsibility to bring the artefacts back to the museum. I will form several teams for this purpose as soon as I complete this meeting. You will need to monitor their investigation to ensure an absolutely foolproof investigation. I assure you that all the necessary logistical support for this case will be taken care of immediately. Spare no expense. I'll personally ensure that we get the necessary monetary support. Utilize all the resources that you need in the Commissionerate. No need for prior approval. I don't want any delay due to red tape and paperwork. Raise any requirement and I will immediately sanction it. I'll also release some advance money and distribute it among you to meet any expenses during the investigation. I'll give you complete operational freedom but ensure results as soon as possible.'

Chaitanya Kumar was fidgeting uncomfortably. Noticing this, the Commissioner asked, 'Chaitanya, do you have something to say?'

'Sir, everything that you said is fine, but there is a high possibility that people might raise objections,' ACP Chaitanya said.

'What do you mean?' the Commissioner asked impatiently.

'For example, people were objecting to the door-to-door search that we did of the buildings adjacent to the museum,' Chaitanya answered, a tad nervously.

'Do whatever you think you need to,' the Commissioner said clenching his fist, with a steely glint in his eyes. 'I'll shoulder complete responsibility for anything done in the process of investigating this case. This task force is the last resort for any criminal investigation. Others may fail, but the task force should never. This is the mantra.'

Anjani Kumar's determination to solve this crime at any cost filtered down to all his team members. They were determined to work tirelessly till the artefacts were recovered. The Commissioner looked around, appraising his team members with his penetrating gaze. He could gauge the positive mood of his team and was pleased. He continued, 'I'm forming teams to analyse the CCTV footage, cell phone data and other activities but, remember, not everything can be solved technically. Irrespective of the technological progress we may have made, human intelligence should remain a critical area of focus. Hence, I want my task force to focus more on intelligence, in addition to monitoring the entire team's progress. So, get your informers on the job. I've ensured that you have access to the required informer network in this area. I want you to use their expertise to quickly solve this case.'

'Definitely, Sir,' the members of the task force said in a determined voice.

'Now, tell me, what additional information did you find at the scene of the crime?' the Commissioner asked, sipping more water and hoping that the rumbling in his stomach wasn't audible.

'Sir, as you already know, the burglary took place in the wee hours of the morning, post-midnight. The CCTV footage from the neighbourhood masjid around that time captured the thieves and is being analysed. It shows two people who came on a bike and entered a house adjacent to the museum. They committed the theft of the precious artefacts and exited in the same manner.'

'Good. So, we know that there were two men involved. Great! Circulate this information. Try to get more information by checking the CCTV footage in various shops and buildings along the possible entry and exit routes.'

After the meeting was over, Anjani Kumar divided his people into teams and assigned them specific tasks. The responsibilities of the various teams were:

1. Checking CCTV footage along the entry route
2. Checking CCTV footage along the exit route
3. Analysing the cell tower dump
4. Verifying the model of the suspects' bike
5. Going over the modus operandi of known criminals with a special focus on offenders who are masons
6. Following up on past museum staff
7. Verifying the houses abutting the museum
8. Tracing the museum visitors
9. Verifying inter-state gangs
10. Verifying history-sheeters zone wise
11. Verifying traders of antique items
12. Verifying staff of college and school housed on the premises
13. Gathering local intelligence

The detective department was given the difficult and time-consuming task of checking the CCTV footage to determine the exit path of the thieves. The task force team, which included ACP Chaitanya and Inspector Madhu, was responsible for monitoring the activities of the newly formed teams. They would work exclusively on the investigation of the burglary till the items were recovered.

After forming the teams, the Commissioner glanced at his watch. It was past 10.00 p.m. The only things he had eaten all day were some onion samosas with Irani tea[18] in the evening. He had wanted to call a meeting with the team leads. But he postponed it to early the next morning.

∽

The next morning, the team leads came to the Commissioner's office at the required time. Without a preamble, the Commissioner began, 'You will collect intelligence as per your assignments. I'll need an update twice a day from all of you individually. I will also hold a review meeting with all the team leads at the end of each day, by 7.30 p.m. I don't want to upset your investigation schedules by having you make the trip to my office every day. Hence, this combined meeting will be a teleconference and you can join from your respective locations.'

Then, he again explained the work distribution to the team and clarified their doubts. After the meeting was over, Anjani Kumar asked his PA to cancel all routine and general review meetings within the Commissionerate. He would need to focus totally on this case till the antiques were recovered. 'Arrange for a video conference with the station house officers[19] and

---

[18]Old City, where the Commissioner was working, is famous for its onion samosas and Irani tea. The latter is a special Hyderabadi dum tea made using reduced milk and tea concentrate.

[19]Station houses are the police stations falling under the Commissioner's territory.

detective teams that I have not spoken to so far,' he instructed his PA.

At the conference, he began by giving them a first-hand update on the case. 'This is a high-profile case and it's shameful that a part of our heritage has been stolen. The police force's pride is at stake here. Remain alert, and check out your informer networks. Inform me immediately if you get any updates. The Old City Station House Officers (SHOs), please be particularly careful. I have a gut feeling that you will be able to collect information from there,' the Commissioner requested.

Throughout the investigation, the Commissioner rigorously conducted these meetings and personally participated in the investigation process along with each team-in-charge to ensure professionalism. Apart from receiving general briefings from all teams, he held a special meeting with this task force every day to mine their expertise in gathering human intelligence.

In the meantime, the detective department had formed four teams to trace the exit route of the thieves. Team 1, under Inspector Purna, was responsible for mapping the possible exit paths of the thieves, identifying the places with CCTV cameras and gathering their footage. He started from the masjid. The thieves could have taken only one road to exit and that was Mir Alam Mandi Road, a long road divided by a dirty, meandering nullah.

Inspector Purna and his team started enquiring at the various houses along the way to check if any of them had installed CCTV cameras. His labours were richly rewarded when he collected footage from two CCTVs showing the thieves moving along the road on their bikes. The first one was outside a house, but, to the Inspector's disappointment, the quality of the footage was poor. However, the other footage came from a colour camera installed outside a shop selling water, and its footage was excellent.

After analysing the footage, Chaitanya Kumar, along with Madhu and Purna, called on the Commissioner at his office. 'Sir, we have identified the model of the thieves' bike. It's a Bajaj Pulsar. And we have a clearer picture of the two men,' Inspector Madhu informed the Commissioner of their finding.

'Can I see the footage?' the Commissioner asked.

'Of course, Sir,' Inspector Madhu took out a pen drive.

'Wait, let's go to a conference room and use the projector,' the Commissioner said. The conference room was right across his office and was equipped with the latest projectors and other state-of-the-art electronic gadgets. Inspector Madhu attached the pen drive to the computer, which was connected to the projector. As the footage played out, the Commissioner saw the two masked men come on a bike. They parked the bike in front of the masjid, their movements unhurried.

'Zoom this part,' Chaitanya Kumar said. 'Okay, rewind a bit. Sir, you can clearly see the bike is a Bajaj Pulsar.'

'Hmm, no license plates?' the Commissioner asked frowning in disappointment.

'No, Sir. Unfortunately, there was no license plate,' ACP Chaitanya responded.

The Commissioner's mobile rang. He checked the caller ID and sent an automated message. While doing this, he kept thinking about what the next steps should be. After a few minutes of silence, when he stared at the screen, he said, 'Okay, you can write to the company that manufactures this bike and check their records. Also, contact the Regional Transport Office (RTO) office to see if they have some photos. We can try to match the photos with those from the CCTV footage. Please get details of this model of bike for the entire Telangana state with the ownership details and contact numbers. Obtain the e-challan particulars of bikes of this model for Hyderabad. Then, verify the ownership details and contact numbers of the owners of the bikes. Simultaneously, compare the photographs of the riders in e-challans with the CCTV footage,' the Commissioner suggested.

'Yes, Sir, we will start immediately,' Chaitanya Kumar, nodded.

'Another thing, Chaitanya. We should withhold this information from the press. This will be our inside information that we will use to nab the thieves at an appropriate time,' the Commissioner suggested as he rubbed his spectacles thoughtfully.

'Yes, Sir, excellent idea,' the ACP nodded again. 'As you can see, Sir, one of them is holding a mobile phone in his hand. We will analyse the cell tower data to check if we can identify the thieves,' the ACP added.

Inspector Madhu cleared his throat, looking at Chaitanya. He was silently asking for permission to speak. Seeing Chaitanya's imperceptible nod, he said, 'Sir, we will also need to get in touch with telecom companies to see if we can get a list of numbers that hit the tower around that time.'

'Yes, good point. You can analyse that data,' Anjani Kumar told Inspector Madhu, mentally applauding his ability. He noted to himself that Inspector Madhu should be given more important work in future. Then, he continued, 'But look how smart these thieves are. They have concealed their identity by wearing a mask and hand gloves to avoid leaving fingerprints.'

'Yes, Sir, but let me show you another piece of footage. This one is in colour. Here, you can see that one of them is lean and the other one is heavy. We guess that the lean guy must have been the one to climb inside and commit the theft,' Inspector Madhu said.

'Well done, but why is there so much delay in checking out the entry and exit routes?' the Commissioner asked, looking at Purna, who had been tasked with this duty.

'Sir, these two men have been captured in several small lanes and by-lanes. But again, this is a time-consuming task. I have just finished mapping the possible paths that could have been taken by the thieves. Next, my team will go door-to-door and try to gather CCTV footage.'

'Sure, great job, Purna!' the Commissioner said warmly.

'Sir, we think that the thieves may be residents of Zahara Nagar. We have footage of the two men on their bike in front of one of the apartments there,' Purna said.

Chaitanya, who knew the area well, said excitedly, 'Which apartment?'

'The one with that Rizvi Canteen, next to that self-help centre, Sir,' Purna responded deferentially. The ACP was at a higher post than him and he was acutely aware of that.

'Oh! That one! We should go and check the backgrounds of the residents of that building and check if their appearance matches that of the two men,' Chaitanya suggested.

'Yes, that makes sense,' the Commissioner said, rubbing his hands. 'Okay, then. You can also look at which cell phone numbers hit the cell tower in that location and try to trace their exit path that way.'

'Sir,' Inspector Madhu, addressed the Commissioner softly.

Anjani Kumar looked at him and asked, 'Yes, Madhu?'

'Sir, I'll go back to inspect the CCTV footage to pinpoint the entry and exit routes. This CCTV footage is from 5.50

a.m. Assuming that the thieves arrived around two–three hours before that, we will collect all the cell IDs from near the mosque, behind the museum and Firoz Sounds, Mandi Road and Zahara Nagar. Then, we will obtain the tower data for all the collected cell IDs and analyse the tower data to trace the progress of the cell phones,' Inspector Madhu explained.

'Yes, good idea, Madhu. Also, check if any of the museum staff had been contacting these cell phones. This could very well be an inside job,' the Commissioner said and Chaitanya nodded in approval.

'Definitely, Sir,' Inspector Madhu said.

'Generally, the thieves would leave the scene of the crime as soon as possible. See which of these cell IDs left the area around the time of the crime and which routes they took,' the ACP added.

'Looks like they were just wandering around trying to confuse us about their exact route. We are trying to see their route after they left the Old City. We have loads of footage to go through. Hence, it is taking time,' Inspector Purna added.

'Okay, keep me posted as soon as you come up with new information,' Anjani Kumar said. He beamed at the men. 'Great work so far!' The men saluted and left to complete the tasks assigned to them.

∽

When Purna, Chaitanya and Madhu came out of the Commissioner's office, all their tiredness had vanished due to the words of praise from the Commissioner. They knew it wasn't easy to earn his praise and hence, they were more than determined to solve the crime at the earliest. Their families were getting upset with their long hours and were worried that they would fall sick. But they were not to be swayed by their families' admonishments and continued to work long hours without any rest.

Inspector Madhu called the administrative heads of several well-known cell phone network providers, asking them for access to their cell tower data.

'Why do you need it? We will need some time to provide the data,' came the stoic responses.

When the matter was escalated to the Commissioner, he said, 'Don't worry, I will get this sorted.'

The Commissioner called up the administrative heads. The effect was immediate. Madhu was granted access to the cell tower data within half a day. He used the C-Dart app developed for the Telangana police to analyse the data.

The Commissioner called a review meeting with the IT team and the task force. He asked Rajashekharan, the head of the IT Team, 'Can you give us a quick summary of what apps we can leverage to identify our criminals? You know, a kind of refresher.'

Rajashekharan, who had come armed with a presentation, started it on the projector. As he began to explain each app in great technical detail, the Commissioner noted that heads were beginning to nod and the eyes of the participants were starting to glaze over. He quickly stopped Rajashekharan.

'Instead of explaining each app in detail, can you explain how we can leverage each of them?'

Rajashekharan paused for a few minutes to gather his thoughts. Then, he said, 'When the team starts analysing the cell tower data, they can use the C-Dart app to find out which of these cell phones belong to known criminals and prepare a list. The list can then be fed to the TSCOP app[20] to get the list of offenders who have committed burglaries of gold and diamonds and are expert wall climbers. Then, the team can feed this shortlisted data into the JRMS (Jail Release Monitoring System) app to find out which of them were out of jail at the time of theft. From the daily review meetings that I have been attending, I get the feeling that the thieves had been planning this crime for some time and had masonry expertise. Most of these criminals start planning their next crime while still in jail. So, we can use the Jail Mulakat app to check if any of the relatives or confederates of these criminals are masons and had been coming to meet them to plan the next crime.'

'Excellent idea! I am sure that the Telangana Police is technologically above other states. Madhu, I suggest you work with Rajashekharan here and take his help when you analyse the cell data.' Madhu fixed a meeting with Rajashekharan immediately after lunch and they got to work analysing the data rapidly.

---

[20]To know more about TSCOP, please see https://bit.ly/3BvzIh2.

6

SOME LEADS DISCOVERED

Mutaali, a rowdy pickpocket with a mile-long criminal history sheet was sitting alone at an Irani café in the Purani Haveli area, mulling over his future. He was thin with a balding head and a patchy greyish beard. Business was terribly slow these days. Younger pickpockets were muscling into his territory. He had three children. His wife, Ibriz, was pregnant with a fourth one, but complications had arisen in her pregnancy. He was in desperate need of money. He was reading *The Siasat Daily* when he came across the news of the theft on the front page. He remembered that Ibriz had nagged him to take her to the museum a few weeks back.

'Why on earth do you want to visit a museum suddenly?' Mutaali had asked Ibriz in surprise. She had been cooking dalcha. The amazing aroma of her dalcha had been wafting out of the tiny kitchen. Mutaali, who was a foodie, had already been drooling in anticipation of his lunch.

'Kaden recently visited with his wife Abida and their children. Abida was telling me there are some beautiful gold, silver and other items there,' Ibriz had told him. She was fed up with her daily life. Taking care of the home and three small children with very little money was not an easy task. Her health problems added to her woes. She had wanted a little break from routine. Being fond of gold, she had gotten interested when she heard that the museum contained gold items.

'If I can't buy real gold items, let me at least see some!' she had exclaimed, looking in frustration at her own tawdry, fake gold bangles and rings.

'But we need to buy tickets to the museum, no?' Mutaali had asked.

Ibriz had sighed heavily and said, 'Why are we always so short of money? Because you don't work enough! You can go and try to earn some money now. But you will sit and read the newspaper. How can you be so selfish?'

Mutaali, who was essentially a peace-loving guy, had caved in, 'Okay, I'll take you to the museum. But you have to wait till I can get some money.'

Ibriz, who was a lot younger, heavier and stronger than her husband, had waved her hand threateningly. 'We will go next week. Get the money by that time. Just stop gambling, okay? Anyway, I'm sure the price of the museum ticket will be cheaper than cinema tickets. And Abida was saying that entry for children below five is free. So, we won't need to buy tickets for the kids.'

Mutaali had suddenly felt violently angry. His face had turned red and spittle had flown out of his mouth as he had yelled, 'Since when did that uncouth bugger Kaden suddenly start visiting museums? Anyway, he can afford to spend money like this. You know that he is a smuggler of antique items. He has more money than me!' Mutaali had felt like killing Kaden. Because of that bugger, he was going to have to take his wife and kids to the museum when money was already tight.

Kaden often insulted Mutaali and treated him like an inferior. Mutaali, in turn, considered him rude and arrogant. There was no love lost between the two men, although their wives were good friends.

The museum trip never happened, as his wife had taken sick. Then, another thought struck Mutaali. *Ah! So, this explains Kaden's sudden interest in museums. He must have gone to recce it.*

'He must have committed the theft, the *madarchod*. I will inform the police about him. Maybe the police will pay me some money for the information,' Mutaali thought out loud.

Mutaali went to the Charminar PS, met Constable Ibrahim and told him about Kaden. He had gotten hold of a picture of Kaden and showed it to the constable.

'Janaab, I've given you a good tip! Won't you give me some money?' Mutaali whined.

Ibrahim looked carefully at Kaden's photo. He was a very fat man and didn't resemble either of the thieves caught on the CCTV footage. Ibrahim didn't think that Kaden was the thief, but he didn't want to antagonize Mutaali. Just to keep the latter happy, he said, 'I will match this with the CCTV footage again. Let me investigate and if I think that Kaden is involved, I'll pay you.'

Mutaali was initially upset, but he soon got over his disappointment. He was sure that Kaden was the thief and that Ibrahim would pay him once it was proven that Kaden had committed the burglary. *He had got that chutiya Kaden's goat!*

Ibrahim immediately called his informer, a waiter at an Irani café, and asked him to keep an eye on Kaden. But he didn't expect any positive results. Kaden's wasn't the only lead the police received. As soon as information about the heist reached the public, there was noticeable excitement among ex-offenders and local bad hats regarding the burglary. The sensational news of the theft soon spread like a wildfire and everyone was eager to learn more about it. Though none of them were aware of the culprits, they were happy about the news, as they, too, wanted to make hay while the sun shone. All rowdy sheeters and property offenders of the Old City, South Zone, East Zone and West Zone tried to find the stolen items on their own. The police were inundated with thousands of false tips and were forced to spend countless precious hours following up on them. Immediately after, the police conducted a counselling session with all local bad hats and property offenders, and they were warned against giving misleading or baseless tips to the police.

∽

Constable Krishna of the Mir Chowk PS was confident that he knew who had committed the crime. '*Mama, mereku malum hai, Aqib hi hoga* (Friend, I know it must be Aqib),' he told his friend, Constable Haider.

'*Kaiko socha re tu aisaich* (Why do you think that)?' Haider asked while scratching his head.

'*Maine chori ka CCTV footage dekha re. Sala chor ka body bilkul usse milte! Aisahi dubla patla hai woh. Ohi hogich* (I saw the CCTV footage of the thief stealing. It is him),' Krishna said, waving his arms around in excitement.

'*Sahi bola re tu. Ohi hogich* (Then you must be right)!' Haider always listened to and agreed with whatever Krishna said. Who else would?

'*O hamesa Charminar ke paas hi rahete. Chal usko pakarke puch tach karte* (He is always loitering around Charminar. Let's catch and interrogate him),' Krishna said, moving to the place where he had parked his bike.

Krishna drove his bike to the Charminar side, Haider riding pillion, and tried to locate Aqib. But, he was missing from his usual haunts around Charminar.

'Wait, I'll ask one of my informers,' Haider told Krishna.

There was a beggar in torn, dirty clothes, sitting with a begging bowl in front of the Mecca Masjid near Charminar. He tried to slink away as soon as he noticed Haider.

Haider quickly caught hold of him and said, 'Oi! Where are you running away? I need to talk to you.'

'Not here, Saab,' the beggar said in an undertone. 'I'll come to your house tomorrow morning.'

The next morning, Haider was shaving, dressed in a lungi and *baniyaan*, when his doorbell rang. Wiping the foam on his cheeks with a towel, he opened the door to find the beggar, whose name was Aslam, standing outside. He was dressed neatly in jeans and a clean shirt. 'As-salaam alaikum,' he said, saluting Constable Haider.

'Walaikum as-salaam, *kya ismart dikhre tu! Boleto ekdum jhakkas! Kisne diye tereko naya kapre* (Hmm, you are looking very smart! Who gave you these new clothes)?' Haider asked.

Aslam smiled but didn't say anything. He kept his eyes lowered and shuffled his feet.

'I want to know about Aqib. Where is he?' Haider continued.

Aslam scratched his head. 'I don't know, Saab. I haven't seen him for a few days.'

'*Ruk ja ek minute* (Wait a minute),' Haider said, closing the door on Aslam's face.

Haider stepped back inside the house and when he reopened the door, he was holding a ₹500 note between his fingers. Aslam's eyes shone at the sight of the note.

'Come now, tell me the truth and this money is yours,' Haider said with a crooked smile.

'Saab, I heard that he has gone to Mumbai. I'll inform you as soon as I see him,' Aslam responded.

'Just now you told me that you didn't know anything about him.'

'Saab, I had forgotten. I suddenly remembered,' Aslam said, scratching his head and looking down at his feet.

Haider decided not to follow up on this obvious lie. Instead, he asked, 'Since when has he stopped coming to the Charminar area?'

'I last saw him at the Friday namaz in Mecca Masjid, Saab. Generally, he has bagara rice and dalcha in Sadab Hotel after that.'

'Is there anybody in Sadab Hotel who knows him?'

'All the waiters know him. He's a regular customer there.'

'Okay. And you have not seen him since Saturday?'

'Yes, Saab.'

'You are telling me the truth this time, right?' Haider asked suspiciously.

'*Allah kasam, Saab* (I swear in the name of God)!' Aslam said, with utmost sincerity.

Haider extended the note. Aslam snapped it up and started shuffling away. Haider called after him, 'Inform me if you hear anything!' before slamming his door shut. With this new piece of information about Aqib's sudden disappearance to Mumbai, Haider thought there was some merit in Constable Krishna's observation that he may have stolen the artefacts from The

Nizam's Museum. Together, Haider and Krishna decided to update ACP Naidu, their station head. They entered the ACP's office and saluted him smartly.

ACP Naidu saluted back and asked, 'So, what happened? You two look very excited.'

The two men updated Naidu. 'Are you sure Aqib has done it? Look, I will take a lot of flak if I catch the wrong guy,' Naidu asked, looking at them sternly.

'We are sure, Sir. He is a master climber. Everybody knows,' Krishna said confidently.

'Okay, go and check out Sadab Hotel once more. You say that he's a regular customer. Also, he is out on bail and has to report to court regularly. He must be in touch with his lawyer. Go and talk to his lawyer,' ACP Naidu ordered.

Haider went to Sadab Hotel. Noor, the waiter, at Sadab Hotel, confirmed that Aqib had had his usual lunch after namaz on Friday.

'Have you seen him after that?' Haider probed.

'No, Saab. But he was saying that nowadays, he is plying his uncle's autorickshaw in Uppal. He came here just to meet his friends. His uncle has met with an accident and is unable to drive. So, Aqib has rented the auto from him to make some money. He was saying that he doesn't have enough money to pay his lawyer,' Noor responded.

'Do you have his uncle's address?'

'No, Sir.'

'Do you have his local address?'

'No, Saab, but he is good friends with Nusrat. They come for dinner together sometimes. You can try to contact her.'

'Where does she stay?'

'She runs a tea stall near the Mecca Masjid.'

'Okay, I will find out,' Haider said, leaving the hotel. He was sure that Aslam, his informer, would know about Nusrat. He went to find Aslam, but he was nowhere to be seen.

'Where is Aslam?' he asked the beggar who generally sat next to him.

'No idea, Saab. Haven't seen him since yesterday,' the beggar responded.

'Have you seen Aqib?'

'Who is Aqib?'

'Arre, that fellow who is short and slim.'

'Oh, that one. Yes, Sir. He has been in Uppal, driving his uncle's autorickshaw for the past few months.'

'Past few months?'

'Yes, Saab. He came for the namaz to Mecca Masjid this Friday. He said that he missed his friends and the bagara rice of Sadab.'

Haider realized that Aslam had cheated him and led him to believe that Aqib had gone underground suddenly. He became furious.

Haider knew where Aslam slept. He went to a small by-lane and found the small plastic tent that Aslam called his home. Aslam was deep in an alcohol- and drug-fuelled sleep.

Haider kicked him and started yelling at him, '*Abe uth! Tereko paisa milne se hi daaru pina chalu* (Get up, you bastard! The moment you get money, you start drinking alcohol)!'

Aslam woke up with a jolt. Sitting up, He rubbed his eyes.

Haider spoke again, '*Aqib Uppal me hai. Tereko bhi malum hai. Mereko ullu banane ki koshis ki tune! Mera paise wapas kar* (Aqib is in Uppal. You know this too! You were trying to dupe me! Return my money)!'

'*Saab, muje malum nahi tha* (Sir, I did not know)!' Aslam responded.

'*Tereko sab malum hai! Tune mereko topi pahanaya! Mere paise wapas kar* (You know everything! You fooled me! Return my money).'

'*Mere paas paisa nahi hai, Saab* (I don't have the money Saab)!'

Haider bent down and searched Aslam's dirty bedding and clothes. He also patted his pockets. No money was to be found.

'*Pura daru me ura diya kya* (Did you blow all the money on alcohol)?'

Aslam scratched his head sleepily, grunted and fell asleep.

Haider kicked him again to wake him up.

'*Nusrat ki chai ki dukan kaha hai* (Where is Nusrat's tea shop)?'

Aslam sleepily gave directions to the location and fell asleep immediately after. Haider gave Aslam a final look of disgust before leaving. *How these people waste their lives,* he thought, exasperated.

He went to speak to Nusrat, who was in her stall, preparing tea. He still needed to verify that Aqib was indeed in Uppal.

'Aqib has stopped doing criminal activities,' Nusrat told Haider earnestly. 'He is running his uncle's autorickshaw in Uppal.'

'Do you have the address?'

Nusrat gave him the address. Haider and Krishna contacted the Uppal PS to confirm that Aqib was really there, although, in their heart of hearts, they had realized that Aqib was not their man.

In the meantime, after watching the CCTV footage of the two thieves escaping with the booty, Inspector Junaid of the Charminar PS was convinced that the thieves must be Kamran and Kasif. They were two brothers, one lean and the other fat. They always operated together and were mainly responsible for small-time burglaries.

He went to their home but found it locked. He returned a few days later to find that the house was still locked. He went to a nearby Irani café, whose owner was his informer.

'Kamran and Kasif? I think that they have moved to Chintalpet with their entire family,' the café owner told Junaid as he watched the kettle of boiling water and added tea leaves to it.

'When did they move?' Junaid asked.

'Around a week ago.'

That would be about the time when the theft occurred, the Inspector thought excitedly.

'Why did they move so suddenly to Chintalpet?' he asked.

'That I can't say, Saab.'

'Okay, can you try to find out where exactly in Chintalpet they moved?'

'I will try Saab, but I cannot guarantee anything.'

'Okay, give me a cup of tea and two onion samosas.' The owner gave Junaid the tea and samosas, which he ate and drank with relish and paid for before leaving.

The Inspector also spoke with his counterpart in Chintalpet. From their conversation, all he could gather was that the entire family seemed to have vanished without a trace. He was convinced about Kamran and Kasif being the culprits. He informed his station head, ACP Nadeem, who was equally excited and passed on the message to the Commissioner, who said, 'That's good work, Nadeem. Try to trace these people as soon as possible. Are they out on bail by any chance?'

'I will check, Sir,' Nadeem said. He called back within an hour to inform the Commissioner that they were indeed out on bail.

'Then, they must report to the court regularly. Try and get hold of their lawyer. He might be able to help,' the Commissioner instructed.

Inspector Junaid, who had a very good informer network, approached a tea stall owner near the High Court. He showed the tea shop owner a photo of the two brothers and asked him to remain alert. This yielded rich dividends. The two brothers came to the court within two days and were immediately nabbed by Inspector Junaid.

'Saab, we didn't commit the burglary, *Allah kasam*. Nowadays, we have opened a chicken shop and by God's grace we can manage,' Kasif said with folded hands.

The two brothers had thick, long hair and long beards. The thieves in the CCTV footage had tonsured heads and clean-shaven faces. It was unlikely that the brothers would have been able to grow such long hair and beards in such a short time. Just to be sure, the Inspector pulled their hair and beards, much to their indignation. They were not fake. Disappointed, he had to let them go.

ᔕ

Another team, headed by Inspector Satish, was in charge of checking out the former employees of The Nizam's Museum. They had started their work. The list of the museum employees and recent ex-employees had already been collected. Inspector

Satish looked at the list and started with the ex-employees.

'I see that Raseed and Salman recently left their jobs. What happened? Why did they leave? And what was their exact role?' he asked the curator of the museum.

'Raseed used to be my secretary, Inspector. He is knowledgeable and helped me catalogue and curate the artefacts in the museum. But, recently, he had a heart attack. That is why he's not coming,' Kalam explained.

'Did he have a heart attack before or after the theft?'

'Around a week before the theft. He was admitted to Apollo Hospital. He is currently out of danger and was discharged from the hospital two or three days ago.'

Apollo is a big corporate hospital and treatment there is pretty expensive. The Inspector wondered how Raseed, with his limited income, could afford to get treated there.

As if reading his thoughts, Kalam said, 'Sir, the Nizam still takes care of us, as we are long-term employees. He paid Raseed's medical bills.' Kalam had a short salt and pepper beard and he kept caressing his beard as he spoke, which distracted Satish a bit.

Satish made a mental note to get this information validated with the Nizam's administrative office, before continuing his questioning, 'What about Salman?'

Kalam suddenly looked quite agitated. He paused for a minute, caressing his beard some more while he carefully thought about how to phrase his words. Then, he nodded to himself, as if he had come to a decision, and said, 'Umm... I don't know how to put this.'

'Don't worry, you can be open with me,' Inspector Satish said encouragingly.

Kalam said, 'Salman was a really bad person, Sir. He was

a security guard. He would sleep on duty and take frequent leaves as well. We tolerated him as long as we could. But, one day, he turned up drunk on duty and misbehaved with a woman visitor. That day, I decided that he had to go. Luckily, the woman didn't file a complaint with the police.'

'Tch, you guys should have encouraged her to file a complaint with the police. I don't understand why the public avoids us. We could have helped. Anyway, was he upset when you fired him?'

'Sure, he was. And he is a local resident. He tried to harass me when I was returning home one day after office.'

'Really? What did he do? Do you want me to go and fix him?' Inspector Satish asked, looking really angry.

'No, no, Sir. I can handle him. Don't bother. Initially, he begged me to take him back on duty. He said that he had kids and a wife and was the sole breadwinner. When I said that I couldn't take him back, he started abusing me. He also threatened me, saying that he'll take revenge. Even now, I feel fearful if I get late here and try to leave this area before dark.'

'Don't worry, I'll fix him. Do you think that he might have stolen the artefacts?'

'I can't say. Maybe. But he's so lazy by nature, I doubt that he would take the trouble of planning and stealing the artefacts.'

'Do his features match the CCTV footage of the thief climbing down into the museum?'

'No, Inspector. He's a tall, heavyset man. But maybe he has a lean, equally crooked partner who helped him with the theft.'

The Inspector looked at the diminutive, intellectual-looking Kalam. He could understand how a man like Salman could have easily intimidated him. Then, he asked, 'Did you ever see Salman with a lean man within the museum?'

'No, but as the thieves seemed to be well-versed with the layout of the room, he may have been involved in some way.'

'Why do you say that?' Inspector Satish asked, feeling excited that Salman could be a potential suspect.

'See, they selected the ventilator right above the CCTV camera, then they twisted the camera away when they climbed down to avoid being captured on the footage. So, they must have had thorough knowledge of the museum. Yes, Salman could be your man!'

'Thanks for this important lead Kalam saab, I will check him out. Do you have his address? And his photo?'

'Let me see if I have it here,' Kalam searched inside his desk and took out a file. He leafed through the documents and said, 'Yes, I have it here.'

Satish took a photo of the address and the passport-size photo of Salman that Kalam produced.

'Any other person you can think of who could have done this?' Satish asked.

'No, Inspector saab.'

Inspector Satish and Constable Sameer arrived at the address given by the curator in plain clothes. Salman lived in a one-room shack in the by-lanes of Mehdipatnam. Inspector Satish saw him sitting outside the shack and recognized him from the photo that the curator had provided. Salman didn't have a criminal record, which was a point in his favour. From the road, the inside of the room was visible and he could see a baby crawling, three toddlers playing and hear another girl crying. A woman was cooking on a gas stove. Both parents were ignoring the children. If he had stolen the artefacts and had obtained money for them, there seemed to be no evidence of it here.

'*Kya re, Salman tera naam hai kya* (Hey, are you Salman)?' Satish asked.

'*Ji, janaab, aap log kaun* (Yes, Sir, who are you)?' Salman responded.

'*Abbe hum tere baap hai* (Oi, I'm the boss of you)! We are the police. We have information that you are responsible for the theft at The Nizam's Museum,' Satish said authoritatively.

'*Dekho Chiccha, baigan ke baataan nakko karo* (Look dude, don't talk gibberish),' Salman reacted angrily.

'*Abe sambhalke baat kar, nahi to abhi andar kar denge tereko* (Talk carefully, else we will put you in jail)!' Constable Sameer warned.

'*Gussa to ayega na? Bina nahi to ka kaam se nikaal diya aur abhi chori ka iljam bhi laga rahe ho* (Why won't I get angry? Not only have they fired me for no reason, they are now accusing me of theft)!' Salman responded.

Considering the way Salman was aggressively talking back to the police, Inspector Satish suspected he may not be a thief. Still, he decided to talk to his counterparts at Mehdipatnam PS and ask them to keep an eye on Salman. But, his sixth sense told him that he had hit a dead end and later, he was proven right.

∽

At the Nampally Police Station, Constable Umar was convinced that the theft was the handiwork of Zahid and Waleed. ACP Srinivas Gunturu, his station head, had informed him that the thieves were suspected to have worked as masons.

'Zahid and Waleed work as masons. When they don't get enough work, they resort to burglaries,' he informed ACP Srinivas.

'Really? Where can you find them? Wait, let me check on the JRMS app. If they are out on bail, their details will be there in the app,' ACP Srinivas said, looking up the details on the app. 'Yes, they were arrested last month for burglary but are now out on bail,' he added, showing the information to Umar on his computer screen.

Srinivas leaned back in his chair and looked at Umar, who was standing stiffly by his side and continued, 'Okay, check at the High Court then. They must regularly attend court and need money to pay their lawyers,' he instructed Constable Umar.

'Yes, Sir, I will try to find out from where they are getting the money,' Umar said.

Umar knew the lawyer who usually represented Zahid and Waleed. His name was Sajid. Umar went to meet him. Sajid was sitting at a table in the corridor of the High Court, talking to some unsavoury looking characters.

'Hello, Sajid bhai, how are you?' Umar asked, approaching him.

'Hi, Umar bhai, you are looking smart! You seem to have lost weight!' Sajid greeted Umar.

'Yes, I fell sick some time back, but I am fine now.'

'So, tell me, what can I do for you?'

'I wanted some information on Zahid and Waleed. Are they attending court regularly?'

'They are royal pains in the ass. They are yet to meet my dues. I feel like punching them sometimes.'

'That means that they are short of money. Looks like they have stopped their criminal activities.'

'Yes, they are now working as masons at a construction site in Gachibowli. They have promised to pay me my dues soon. That is why I tolerate them.'

Umar coordinated with the Gachibowli PS and confirmed that Zahid and Waleed had really turned a new leaf and were now working at a construction site.

ↄ

Inspector Ravi of the task force was convinced that the theft had been committed by a person who had inside knowledge about the museum. 'That attendant, Farhan, he is a very shifty looking fellow. Did you see how he was shaking with fear on the day of the theft? And he was incharge of the hall from where the artefacts were stolen. He had the keys and all. If he was innocent, why was he afraid?' he asked his colleague, Sheshu, who had no response and simply shook his head.

'I'm going to the museum to keep a close watch on all the staff members for the next few days,' Inspector Ravi added.

'If you are going there, keep your eyes open and monitor all the security guards as well. They have been trained to look for weak spots. Why didn't they advise the museum staff that anybody could come in through the ventilator?' Sheshu suggested.

Sheshu was quite a sharp person and a good judge of character as well. Ravi picked his brain quite often. He nodded in agreement and said, 'I've heard that this security agency has been employed by the museum recently. I doubt they bothered to check the previous guards.'

'Yes, really, the security was so pathetic! The museum was literally begging to be robbed,' Sheshu said, shock written large on his face. 'How could the trust have not done more to secure the museum when such precious items have been kept there?'

Ravi nodded his head sagely and speculated, 'Probably

lack of funds. Most of the Nizam's vast wealth is disputed with no clear inheritor. Hard to imagine that at one time the last Nizam of Hyderabad was the wealthiest man in India.'

A recent *India Times* article stated that Osman Ali Khan's net worth was estimated at over ₹17.47 lakh crore ($230 billion) after adjusting for inflation. His net worth is almost near the net worth of Elon Musk, the world's richest man as of 2022, with a net worth of $286 billion. Osman Ali Khan had a personal gold collection worth over $100 million and owned over $400 million worth of jewellery, including a diamond the size of a tennis ball, which, it is rumoured, he used as a paperweight.[21]

Ravi and Sheshu spent the next few days at the museum. They also took the opportunity to look around the place, noting all the priceless gold artefacts studded with huge emeralds, diamonds, rubies and other precious items with awe. After that, for a few days, they stood near the crime scene, pretending to take notes while keeping a close eye on the staff.

'Do you see how Farhan is always scared? I'm sure that he has helped the thieves. An innocent man wouldn't be so scared,' Ravi said while they were eating lunch at the local restaurant, which was famous for its biryani.

'True. The other day, I saw him whispering to Rizvi. Maybe these two men committed the theft together,' said Sheshu as he bit into a juicy chicken leg with relish.

'Yes, and Rizvi is so thin, he could easily pass through the narrow ventilator,' Ravi concurred.

---

[21]Tiwari, Anuj, 'Not Ambani or Adani – This Nawab of Hyderabad Was the Richest Man in India Ever!', *India Times*, 20 April 2022, https://bit.ly/3RuaNQK. Accessed on 30 September 2022.

Sheshu stopped eating suddenly as Ravi's idea resonated with him. Putting down the chicken leg, he said, staring at Ravi, 'You have a great point there. Let's do one thing. Let's call them to the police station separately and interrogate them.'

'Yes, let's call them late at night to the police station. That will put the fear of God in them,' Ravi concurred.

In the meantime, Farhan, the attendant, was really scared. He had noticed the police looking at him suspiciously day after day. He began to feel sick and lost interest in food. He and his wife had no children and thus, there was no support system to help or guide them. His wife, Nazia, suffered from diabetes and hypertension.

Ya Allah! What have we done wrong? Why does my husband need to go through so much pain and tension when he has never done anything wrong in his life? Nazia thought, praying to God constantly.

'What will happen if they fire you, thinking that you may be the thief? We don't even have enough savings and nobody to turn to,' Nazia said, sobbing.

'Don't worry. The curator has assured me that nobody suspects me,' Farhan said, trying to console his wife.

In reality, none of the museum staff was talking to each other much. They all looked tense and worried. Farhan hoped and prayed that he wouldn't lose his job. After working for 16 long years in the museum, he had no idea what he would do or where he would go if he was fired.

A few days later, Farhan got a call from the Mir Chowk PS. 'Is this Farhan's number?' the man at the other end asked authoritatively.

'Yes, this is Farhan,' he said, his heart suddenly starting to flutter. Somehow the tone of the man at the other end made him nervous.

'We are calling from the Mir Chowk Police Station. Can you come over now?'

'Now, S...sir? It's 9.00 p.m., Sir!'

'This is a very serious investigation. The police are working day and night to solve this case. You need to come when we call you! Is that clear? I expect you to be in the police station in half an hour,' Inspector Ravi barked over the phone before disconnecting.

Farhan began to cry. Seeing him, his wife started crying and said, 'What will happen now, Farhan? What will they do to you?'

'I don't know, Begum! The other day, Rizvi was saying that the police have done a few encounter killings. I hope that they don't encounter me and blame me for the theft,' Farhan said wiping his eyes.

'Don't say such things! I've nobody else other than you. We don't even have kids. I'll also die along with you,' Nazia said, crying piteously.

Farhan wiped her eyes. 'Don't cry, Begum. Maybe they'll just question me and let me go. I had better leave for the police station now.'

'I'll come with you.'

'Don't talk nonsense! How can you come so late in the night to the police station? You stay at home and pray for me.'

When Farhan reported to the Mir Chowk PS, Inspector Ravi deliberately kept him waiting in the reception area. This was a common tactic used by the police to unnerve suspects in the hope that they would slip up during interrogation. After keeping him waiting for half an hour, Inspector Ravi came to meet him.

He was deliberately hostile and didn't return Farhan's greeting. Instead, he asked him to get into a police patrol car and after they had driven to a deserted spot, he turned to Farhan and said, 'We have inside information that you and Rizvi were involved in the theft. If you come clean about your role in the whole business, we'll try to help you get a lenient sentence. But, if you don't confess now and Rizvi points his finger at you, we'll be merciless in our treatment.'

Farhan nearly wet his pants. Folding his shaking hands in front of the policeman, he said, 'Saab, saab, I may be a poor person, but I'm totally honest. I've never committed any theft in my life. *Allah kasam!* Please let me go!'

'So, you won't tell us about Rizvi's involvement?'

'I've no idea whether Rizvi is involved, Sir. But I can definitely say that I'm not involved. Please let me go home, Sir. My wife is sick and needs me,' Farhan pleaded and began sobbing in earnest.

Inspector Ravi looked at him sternly. Finally, he said, 'Today I'll let you go. But remember, you'll wish you had never met me if I find out that you were involved in the theft.'

'I'm innocent, Sir. Please let me go,' Farhan begged, keeping his hands folded in front of the Inspector.

'If not Rizvi, who do you think stole the items?' Ravi demanded.

Farhan racked his brain in desperation. He knew that the police wouldn't let him go unless he gave them some leads. Then, he remembered the two fellows who had come to the museum a few days back. Feeling relieved, he said, 'Saab, two scruffy-looking men came to the museum a few days back.

They didn't want to shell out money for the entry tickets and even fought with Atif and Rizvi.'

'Who is this Atif?'

'Sir, Atif is the man who sells entry passes for the museum at the ticket counter.'

'So, Rizvi came when he heard the altercation between them?'

'Yes, Janaab. The two men finally paid for the tickets and were allowed to go inside the museum.'

'Describe their appearance. Did either of them look like the thief caught on the CCTV camera of the museum?'

'Sir, I don't exactly recall, but one of them was very thin and could have easily slid through that narrow ventilator.'

'Okay, report to the police station tomorrow, I'll arrange for a sketch artist. You can describe the two men. Get Rizvi along, and together you can describe them to the sketch artist.'

The next day, Ravi personally went and checked the footage of the last 30 days that they had gotten from the museum cameras. He called Rizvi and Farhan. They were also asked to identify the two men. These men looked similar to the two men whose footage had been captured in the CCTV camera at the mosque, but there was no way they could trace two random men who had happened to be inside the museum a few days before the crime took place.

Inspector Ravi, a veteran of the police force, realized that Farhan was too much of a scaredy cat and didn't have the mental disposition to commit such a daring theft. Disappointed, he let Farhan go. He had formed a similar opinion about Rizvi when he had interrogated him. He hoped that the sketches that the two men helped make would yield some results when he distributed the leaflets in the locality of the museum.

∽

The investigation of the cell IDs had also led nowhere. The application of the Telangana police department for cell tower data analysis and the C-Dart app had not yielded any results.

Six days after the theft, every effort by the police teams seemed to be coming to nought. 'I am afraid the thieves have escaped from Hyderabad—most probably to Mumbai. One of my informants told me, but let us keep this to ourselves for now until we verify this information,' Inspector Madhu told ACP Chaitanya in a one-to-one meeting.

On a side note, though, the vehicle checks had brought in unexpectedly rich rewards. Around midnight one night, Constables Ramakrishna and Vikram were dozing off at an isolated checkpoint set up at the Hyderabad–Rachakonda border, which was a forest reserve area. Hearing the sound of an approaching vehicle, they woke up with a start. The driver of the vehicle was clearly startled to see the constables. He accelerated and would have nearly run them over had they not jumped back in time. Ramakrishna immediately called the next checkpoint and the driver was apprehended there. He turned out to be on the most-wanted list for hash and marijuana smuggling in the Telangana area. Similarly, another noted sandalwood smuggler was caught during the random vehicle checks.

Ghulam and Badshah, oblivious to the ongoing investigation, were in possession of riches beyond their wildest imagination.

7

CRIMINAL MASTERMINDS: KHOONI BADSHAH AND GHULAM

Muhammad Badshah Pasha, also known as Khooni Badshah, was the son of an autorickshaw driver, Muhammad Mahmood Pasha. He had six brothers and two sisters. In his early childhood, his mother had given him the pet name 'Aayan', meaning 'God's gift', but that name didn't stick for long because he turned out to be the Devil's spawn.

Ever since he was a boy, he fought with and bullied other kids his age. His favourite place to loiter around was a nearby beef shop. One day, the beef seller grew irritated with the young Badshah and yelled at him, 'Kya re? Idhar kiu ghum phir raha hai? Bhag yiha se (Oi! Why are you loitering around here? Go away)!'

'Give me one small piece of meat, please,' Badshah pleaded.

The meat seller took pity on the small boy and gave him a small piece of meat. To his surprise, the boy started eating the raw meat. He exclaimed in disgust, 'Arre! Kya kar raha hai tu? Kutta billi ke jaisa kaccha gosht kha raha hai? Tera naam to Khooni hona chahiye re (Why are you eating raw meat like a dog or cat? Your name should be Khooni)!'

Despite his initial repulsion, it was entertaining for the meat seller to see a little boy eating raw meat. Thus, he had started giving the young Badshah scraps of meat regularly. Ever since, Muhammad Badshah Pasha started being known as 'Khooni Badshah'. Only his mother had continued to call him 'Aayan'.

As Badshah grew older, he became increasingly aggressive. His neighbours would complain about him to his mother. At night, when his father came home, his mother would report Badshah's misdeeds to his father, who would beat the boy black and blue every night. Despite this, neither did Badshah ever improve nor did his parents learn that hitting a child never helps.

With time, Badshah grew even more aggressive. He lost interest in his studies and became the worst student in his class at school. It didn't help that both his parents were illiterate, and his father couldn't afford a tutor for him.

Then, one day, he fought with the Head Boy for reporting him to the Principal. He beat the boy, who was almost twice his age, so severely that the latter had to be hospitalized for two months. The Principal, who had never liked Badshah and considered him to be a bad influence on the rest of the kids, took this opportunity to rusticate him. Badshah was happy at this turn of events. He would never have to study again. He knew he would be severely beaten when his father learnt of his latest escapade, but he didn't care. He had gotten used to the beatings.

To his surprise, his father didn't beat him that night. After dinner, Senior Pasha called him and made him sit by his side. Badshah sat down, feeling ill at ease, wondering when the slaps would start landing on him. Instead, his father said gently, 'I'd been thinking about what to do with you for some time. You are failing every year, and I can no longer afford to pay your school fees. I don't think that you have any aptitude for studies anyway. You'll learn construction work and start earning from now. Tomorrow, I'll take you to my friend, Ali. He's an expert in construction work, particularly centring. You'll train with him. Do you understand what I am saying?'

Badshah nodded mutely.

'Good, you can go now,' his father said.

That night, Badshah slept peacefully. His body was not aching from beatings, and he would never have to go back to that horrible school. *Who the hell studied anyway?* All he wanted to do in life was earn money.

The next morning, Badshah started going to the construction site. By the time he was 18, he became an expert mason. But he wasn't happy. He wanted to grow rich and fast. He was inspired by Bollywood movies, including *Once Upon a Time in Mumbai, Don* and others that glorified gangsters. The dirt and dust of construction sites exasperated him. On Sundays, he didn't work. He hung out with his friends on the omnipresent boulders in and around Rajendra Nagar, where he stayed.

One Sunday evening, he was sitting with his friend, Abdul. He had quarrelled with the supervisor of the construction site where he had been working. He had been feeling lazy the past few days and had played hooky from work without any prior intimation. Fed up with his irregular and aggressive habits, the supervisor paid him off and fired him. Badshah bought beef with part of that money, some of which he ate raw, despite his mother's admonishments. The rest of the money, he spent on *ganja* and alcohol.

His father was now scared of him and could no longer beat him up. His parents implored him to ask for the supervisor's forgiveness and report back to work. But their pleas fell on deaf ears. Badshah cursed them and went out to get drunk. Then, he spent the entire Sunday sleeping. In the evening, he met his friends over some more alcohol.

'*Yeh mera life jo hai na ekdom chutiya life hai* (What a miserable life I am leading)! I am not going to work for that *harami* supervisor anymore. What does he think of himself?' Badshah exclaimed angrily to his friends.

'Yes, Ustaad! There are better ways of earning easy money!' Abdul, his friend, said in a low voice after looking around to check that nobody was nearby, overhearing their conversation.

'Like what?' Badshah asked curiously.

'Shh…not so loud,' Abdul said, glancing around again. Then, he almost whispered, 'Ustaad, Ali and I have started a new business. You know that I'm driving a rented auto. Ali pretends to be a passenger. Then, he steals mobiles from his fellow passengers. We sell the mobiles at about ₹500 to ₹600 per piece. We get a higher price if the mobiles are high-end models.'

'*Nako bolo* (Don't tell me)! Wow! How much are you guys earning?' Badshah whispered back, excited.

'Anywhere from ₹3000–₹5000 per day. Why don't you join our gang?' Abdul responded.

From that day onwards, Badshah became a petty criminal. Burglary became his speciality. He started earning good money, which he spent on alcohol and women.

But all good things must come to an end. One day, he entered a house in Rajendra Nagar to burgle it. He had done the recce of the house for the past week and knew that the owner wasn't home. But, unfortunately for him, the owner came home the very night that he had planned the burglary. The owner had come back early from a party and walked in on Badshah while he was committing the theft. The owner also happened to be a karate champion and beat him black and blue before calling the police.

He was beaten again by the Rajendra Nagar police in their lock-up. He was granted bail but couldn't afford to pay the bail amount and was incarcerated in the Chanchalguda Jail.

He reached the jail at around 2.00 p.m. When he entered through its gates, he was dispirited, dejected, sick and hungry. He was asked to stand in an extremely slow-moving queue and wait. A police officer completed his paperwork and then, he had to join another queue where, after another interminable wait, his fingerprints were taken. At every step of the various processes, he was made to wait. During one such wait, a fellow prisoner came near him and whispered in his ears, 'Give me all your money, else I'll kill you in jail.'

Though Badshah was scared, there was nothing he could do, as he had no money. 'I don't have any money,' he stammered.

The man forcibly took his wallet, which had ₹10 in it. The police officer standing nearby pretended not to notice. The man took the small sum, spat on the floor and said, '*Chutiya saala, bhikhari kahika* (You idiot! You bloody beggar)!' Then, he stuffed Badshah's wallet back into his pocket.

Next, Badshah was asked to strip down to his underwear by a brutal police officer. After a thorough search, the officer barked, 'Cough!' After ensuring that he had not smuggled any items in his body parts, he was given a prison uniform, a blanket and toiletries.

Once the formalities were done, a tough police officer came

in and addressed the new prisoners, 'Don't try to play around with us. If you don't abide by the rules, you'll straight away go to the hospital on a stretcher. Don't try any mischief with us.'

Upon hearing this stern speech, Badshah nearly wet his pants. Then, he and the other newly incarcerated inmates were sent to another gate. Upon entering it, he found himself in a compound with a small garden and a tap for washing clothes. Some prisoners were watering the plants and some were washing clothes. All the new arrivals were greeted with lewd comments and he felt even more dejected and wished with all his heart that he had never committed the crime. Someone called out, '*Naya bakre aye re* (A new victim has come)!'

Some of the inmates who arrived with him were greeted like old friends and, later on, Badshah realized that they had already spent time in jail before. When he was led to his cell, his cellmates looked happy to see him. One of them patted his head and said, '*Eh! Chikna aya re* (Hey, look at this hottie)!' Another slapped his shoulder and said, '*Naya maal aya* (Fresh meat has arrived)!' They surrounded him and grabbed the meagre toiletries he had been given. They pinched his cheeks and hurled curses at him as he flinched and tried to protect himself from their onslaught.

Initially, he was given the worst prison jobs, like toilet cleaning. As he had to clean the toilets, he was allowed to take a bath at the end. Many times, there was not enough water for him to take baths and he had to spend the day smelly and unwashed.

Badshah soon learned the ways of the prison. The leader among the inmates was a criminal named Prakash, and Badshah soon realized that he had to appease Prakash if he wanted to survive jail. Badshah was young, strong and aggressive. So, Prakash made him his bodyguard. Badshah's job was to beat up anybody who didn't agree with Prakash, who was a sadist and enjoyed boxing. He would pit one inmate against another. Badshah, being young and strong, was his favourite. The jail authorities knew of all these unauthorized activities, yet looked the other way. Despite the difficulties, Badshah soon adjusted to prison life, and even thrived under it, as he unleashed his pent-up frustrations upon some hapless victims in these boxing bouts.

After two years he was released from jail. He was given a hero's welcome by his mohalla friends, some of whom had served jail terms too. Only his family was unhappy. He had changed. Prison had hardened Badshah and people seemed to be afraid of him. Badshah saw the fear in his family's eyes for the first time and he was smugly satisfied.

His first act after being released was committing another burglary, for he no longer feared prison. The next time he was caught and jailed, he was prepared. He had made friends with some of the folks who were serving long terms. They welcomed him back. But, this time, the leader had changed. Prakash had been murdered and the new leader was Usama, a fat yet immensely strong man. His skin was the colour of coal and his eyes bloodshot. Later, Badshah came to know that he was serving life imprisonment for committing murder. He also came to know that Usama loved young boys. He particularly liked Badshah. After resisting his advances for some time, Badshah finally had to give in. He knew that he had to tolerate Usama's advances if he were to survive in jail. Eventually, he even came to like it and came out as bisexual later in life. Usama became his mentor. Realizing that he was a big-time criminal and was given some privileges, like a cell phone, which he used to deal drugs, made Badshah admire Usama even more.

Thus, Badshah's life went on—he would commit thefts, get caught, spend some time in jail and go back to a life of crime as soon as he was released. He even started a romantic relationship with one of his gay friends. When his father came to know about his homosexual tendencies, he got Badshah married to his friend's daughter, Rubina, in the hope that marriage would cure him of his bad habits. Badshah was happy for a few months. Then, he started drinking again. He would come home drunk and beat up Rubina.

Unable to bear these daily assaults, his pregnant wife left him and filed a case against him. Badshah didn't give a damn. One more case would only add shine to his illustrious criminal career. He continued to visit male prostitutes and spent money lavishly on them, inspired by the glamourous lifestyles of the criminals in Bollywood movies.

One day, when he was fighting with his father, the old man said bitterly, 'If you had to become a thief, at least you could have become a big shot thief. Now you will die on the street like any other petty criminal.'

Badshah, who generally disregarded whatever advice his father gave him, thought that his words had some merit this time. He began to seriously consider how he could become a big-time criminal—like Usama, his hero.

ᔐ

Ghulam, also known as, Muhammad Ghulam, was 24 years old when he became a petty thief. He started his criminal career much later than Badshah, but he began with a bang—by stealing the Nizam's gold tiffin box and other priceless historical artefacts worth over ₹50 crore.

Ghulam was the youngest child of Muhammad Aziz and hence, the most spoilt. Aziz would beat his eldest son and even his daughter, but Ghulam was always spared the rod. Ghulam was very fair with sharp features and was a cute-looking boy. He was also docile. Needless to say, he was the apple of his father's eye. Though Ghulam was sharp and intelligent, he had no interest in academics. He had been enrolled in a local Urdu-medium school, but after failing in the first grade and again, in the second grade, he gave up his studies. As a manager in a local hotel, Aziz was very busy, so it fell upon Ghulam's illiterate mother to educate him and his siblings. She didn't care much for education and wanted the boys to start earning as soon as possible.

So, Ghulam and his elder brother, both teenagers, were put to work as apprentices with a welder. Soon, they mastered the art and became professional welders. When Ghulam was 21 years old, he was married to a woman named Zeenat, who had a previous lover. Thus, it was an unhappy marriage. After separating from her, Ghulam took a loan of ₹80,000 and went to Saudi Arabia via an agent. When he landed in Saudi, he didn't have a work permit. He had to work as an illegal immigrant and hence, was at the mercy of his employers. He got a welding job where he had to work like a slave at all hours. He barely had time to eat and the food was also sub-standard. At the end of the month, when he asked for wages, he was told that he would be paid at a later date. Ghulam seethed with rage, but there was very little he could do. Six months went by, and he was not given any wages. The unscrupulous businessman who employed him took full advantage of the fact that Ghulam didn't have a work permit and kept putting off his payments. Finally, Ghulam realized that he was being exploited. He decided to go to Mecca. There, he helped pilgrims, and the tips that he got in return enabled him to eke out a living.

At Mecca, Ghulam came across a Pakistani national, Zoaib, who had also come to Saudi Arabia without a work permit. A rivalry developed between the two men over the collection of tips from the pilgrims. One day, their animosity turned ugly and they started brawling on the streets of Mecca. The police arrested them for disorderly conduct and when they were found to be illegal immigrants, both Zoaib and Ghulam were jailed and later deported.

When Ghulam landed in Mumbai, he was an embittered and frustrated man. He had only around ₹1 lakh in his pocket. When he had taken the loan for ₹80,000 to pay the agent and had travelled to Saudi, he had dreamt that he would return a rich man. Instead, he had barely enough to repay his loan. But the silver lining was that upon returning to Hyderabad, he reconciled with his wife, and they rented a house in Rajendra Nagar, close to his parents' house. Soon, his wife was pregnant, and Ghulam started doing odd jobs. Eventually, along with his brother, he opened a shop selling paan, cigarettes and tea.

Badshah and Ghulam's lives had occasionally crossed paths when they played together as kids, but they had lost touch, though they both stayed in Rajendra Nagar and were, in fact, distant relatives. They met again at a *nikkah* (wedding) ceremony at another cousin's place and rekindled their friendship. This meeting turned out to be momentous for both men. There was an instant chemistry between the two. Badshah introduced Ghulam to drugs and they started regularly smoking marijuana together.

∽

Zeenat and Ghulam were fighting in their home.

'Why does that man Badshah keep coming to our house?' Zeenat demanded. 'He has no *tameez* (manners). The way he stares at me when you are not looking makes my flesh crawl.'

'*Arre nahi*, he's a good fellow! You are always criticizing members of my family. I don't object when your family members visit us,' Ghulam countered.

'My family members come with *tohfas* (gifts). Not like this uncouth person. No, he is not a good man! I'm telling you, get rid of him. He's bad news,' Zeenat declared. She loved to boss over Ghulam, who usually meekly listened to her. Not this time, though.

'Shut up! I said he's a good man. Don't bad-mouth him in front of me ever again!' Ghulam snapped.

Zeenat stared at Ghulam. This was the first time he had disagreed with her and been rude to her.

'How dare you, Ghulam! How can you talk to me like that! It's all that Khooni Badshah's bad influence. Everybody in the family knows that he is a stupid thief. He has gone to jail so many times. You'll also end up in jail with him if you aren't careful,' Zeenat screamed at Ghulam.

Ghulam got to his feet and slapped Zeenat hard across the face. 'I told you not to bad-mouth Badshah. Learn to respect him.'

Zeenat stared at Ghulam in shock. He had never hit her before. She started bleeding out from the corner of her mouth.

She wiped it with her chunni feeling more shocked than in pain. Whatever happened to the mild-mannered, charming man she had married? He had lost interest in her in bed as well. What was going wrong with her husband?

'It's all that Khooni Badshah's fault. What *jadu tona* (black magic) he has performed on you, I don't know,' she sobbed.

'Arre, he's a good man, I keep telling you. Now, will you shut up? Or should I shut you up?' Ghulam asked threateningly.

The next morning, Zeenat complained to Ghulam's parents. His parents were kind and supportive. Her mother-in-law applied some ice to her bruised face and generally fussed over her, cursing her son for treating his wife this way. 'Ghulam was such a gentle child. How could he do this to you?' she asked patting the ice water dry tenderly with a towel.

Ghulam's father said, 'I too have been noticing a change in Ghulam since the day he rekindled his friendship with Badshah. I never liked Pasha's family. I've always maintained my distance from them. I've heard really bad things about Badshah. But now Ghulam is grown up and knows his mind. I doubt he will listen to me, but I'll speak to him.'

Despite these words of comfort, Zeenat's sixth sense told her that Ghulam would ignore his parents' advice. The corrupt influence of Badshah was evident. 'That man must have done some jadu tona on my Ghulam. See if we can get a fakir to help him,' she said in despair.

But no fakir would be able to save Ghulam from the devil-incarnate that was Khooni Badshah.

8

PLANNING THE HEIST

In 2018, Ghulam got electrocuted while doing some welding at a construction site in Gachibowli. He fell unconscious, and there were entry and exit burn marks. The other workers took him to a nearby hospital, where he was treated and discharged. But for some time after the accident, he felt frail and was unable to go to work. As a result, the construction supervisor promptly replaced him with another welder. Without a job, he started spending most of his time with Khooni Badshah. They started spending their evenings together, drinking and doing drugs. During these sessions, Badshah would regale Ghulam with glamourized accounts of his various escapades, committing bike thefts, burglaries and other petty crimes.

Under Badshah's influence, Ghulam, who had never indulged in alcohol or drugs, developed a taste for both. He also started smoking marijuana, finding that it helped ease the body pain he had been feeling since his accident at the construction site. Badshah soon became Ghulam's hero. He would talk about how he would be a millionaire one day. He already wore expensive Zara jeans and Skechers shoes worth at least ₹15,000. He even had a stolen Rolex watch and the latest Samsung phone worth at least ₹50,000. He drove an expensive bike and he would zip through the roads as if he owned them. Most of his acquaintances were afraid of him. Younger men would admire his swagger. His swashbuckling character and aggressive and audacious personality, which were the polar opposite of Ghulam's nature, fascinated and awed him. He dreamt of emulating Badshah but could never imagine reaching his level.

Even though the doctors in the hospital had given Ghulam a clean bill of health, he continued to have breathing difficulties and suffered muscular spasms in his arms. He went to a local doctor in Rajendra Nagar, who advised him, 'You should visit the Princess Durru Shehvar Children's and General Hospital in Purani Haveli. They have the latest equipment. You need to get an MRI done; you will get the cheapest rates there.'

When Ghulam went to the hospital, he was asked to join a queue where tokens were being distributed. The counter was closed, and a notice hung over it. Since Ghulam couldn't read English, he asked the man behind him in the queue about what the notice said.

The man replied, 'It says the counter will open at 9.00 a.m.'

Ghulam had come to the hospital without having any breakfast. He was feeling hungry and miserable. So, he asked the man, 'Would you mind keeping my position in the queue? I'll quickly eat something and come.'

Seeing Ghulam's weakened state, the man agreed. After eating at the nearby Madras Café, Ghulam felt better. He peeked through the iron gate of the hospital. The counter had still not opened.

He decided to explore the area. He took the lane next

to the hospital and saw a board in Urdu that pointed in the direction of The Nizam's Museum. Typically, Ghulam avoided museums and such like the plague. But today, he was so bored that he decided it would be as good a place as any to while away his time. It was 10.15 a.m. and the place was empty. Ghulam paid ₹50 as the entry fee and went in.

Feeling a bit nervous, he hesitantly climbed the wooden staircase and entered the museum. Soon, all his nervousness was forgotten at the sight of the silver and gold items on display. He wandered around, staring wide-eyed at all the wealth on display. He estimated that the items on display would be worth crores of rupees. He started to feel bitter. Here he was, struggling to pay his medical bills, yet there was so much money just lying around in a worthless museum. Life was unfair, indeed! His eyes fell on the Holy Quran, which was bound in a solid gold box. He was captivated by the beautiful, glittering item and itched to feel it with his own hands and take it with him. After staring enthralled at the stunning piece for about five minutes, he sighed and moved on. He wandered about the museum for the next two hours before realizing that he was getting late for the hospital.

The queue had vanished by the time he went back to the hospital. The coupons were no longer available, but he didn't care.

That evening, when he met Badshah, he could talk about nothing but the items on display at The Nizam's Museum.

'*Nakko bolo! Yeh madarchod logo ke pas itna paise hai* (You don't say! These motherfuckers have so much money)!' Badshah exclaimed.

'Yes, and here we are struggling for a few rupees,' Ghulam said bitterly, taking a sip of his drink.

The Holy Quran kept in an exquisitely crafted gold box

Source: The Hyderabad Police

Badshah looked at Ghulam hesitantly. He was worried that Ghulam might take offence at what he was about to suggest. Then, he put his hesitation aside and said, 'Let's try to steal some gold from the museum.'

'Oh no, no! My parents will kill me!' Ghulam said, in wide-eyed fear.

But, as the evening went by, they drank some more and Ghulam got more light-headed with each drink, the idea began to grow on him. He hit his left hand with his right fist. 'I say, Ustaad. Let's steal some of the artefacts. In Saudi, they will fetch huge money. But I'll do the planning. This needs a lot of thinking and planning. *Jo hoga so dekh lenge* (We will handle the things as they happen).'

'Madarchod, can't I plan? What are you implying? Am I a fool?' Badshah demanded angrily. He turned even more aggressive than usual when he was drunk.

'Arre, nahi, nahi, Ustaad! Of course, I didn't mean it that way. You are the best! You are crafty and ingenious. Of course, you are. But you have such a good body and smart clothes that you stand out in a crowd. I need to go to the museum at least two-three more times. We need someone who can blend into the crowd. After all, we are not locals in the Old City. Every eye will be on us,' Ghulam pacified Badshah.

'Hmm,' Badshah was mollified.

'Well, I'll go and check out the locality. I'll see what can be taken easily. Let me think some more about this. Please, Ustaad, don't get upset with me!'

'Okay, *mere bhai* (my brother),' Badshah hugged him. Growing mushy, he added, 'You are closer to me than my own brothers. I'll wait for your green signal.'

The next day, Ghulam was a bundle of nerves. The previous evening, he had been feeling particularly sick and under the influence of alcohol, stealing the precious artefacts from the museum had seemed like a very good idea. But now that he was sober, he was having second thoughts. Regardless, he decided to visit the hospital in Purani Haveli again. He would do a recce of the museum while he was there.

Visiting the museum this time, he paid close attention to detail. The security in the museum appeared to be pretty lax. A fat security guard was snoozing by the entrance, his substantial body supported by an insubstantial plastic stool. On the first floor, another security guard sat, bored and unmindful of the visitors.

Ghulam went straight to the section displaying the gold

artefacts. He noted the CCTV cameras. If he had to steal, he would take the most valuable items possible. However, the artefacts had to be small so that he could easily carry them away in his bag. After careful consideration, he decided on stealing a gold tiffin box encrusted with diamonds, a gold cup and saucer and a spoon. All of these had rubies and emeralds embedded in them. He also wanted the Quran, which was bound with gold. His eyes glinted at the very sight of these artefacts as he surreptitiously took photos of the items on his mobile, taking care that his activities weren't caught on camera and glancing around to check if the guards could see him. However, he needn't have worried, as the guard was snoozing in the corridor outside and paid no attention to him.

The gold cup, saucer and spoon that were stolen from the museum

Source: The Hyderabad Police

The gold tiffin box that was stolen from the museum

Source: The Hyderabad Police

Inside the museum

Source: The Hyderabad Police

The corridor outside the museum halls housing the artefacts

Source: The Hyderabad Police

Ghulam went to the museum around 10.30 a.m. on a Wednesday. There were no visitors around then. He looked around the room, thinking about how he could enter. As he scouted the place, he noticed several ventilators near the ceiling of the vast hall. There was a CCTV camera directly above one of the ventilators, pointed at the display unit with the tiffin box. He wondered what was on the other side of the ventilator. He could see some sunlight filtering through the vent. *This must lead to the terrace outside,* he thought excitedly. He exited the room. The ceiling of the corridor outside was much lower than the roof of the room displaying the artefacts. The corridor had windows, and he could see two dried trees right outside. He went back inside and loitered back to the first hall, which was closer to the curator's office.

As he was studying the silver artefacts displayed there, he heard a person asking the guard outside, '*Curator saab hai* (Is the curator in his office)?'

'Siyaam bhai! *Sab khairiyat* (Is everything okay)?' the guard enquired.

'Arre nahi! CCTV cameras are getting old. I need to discuss this with the curator.'

Ghulam grew alert. He had sharp ears. He listened with full concentration while pretending to study the silver items on display. The door of the curator's office was open, and he could hear Siyaam walking into the office.

The curator said, 'Siyaam, tell me, how can I help you?'

'Janaab, one of the CCTV cameras is not working. Also, we need to upgrade the cameras.'

'Siyaam, you know that money is tight. Why are you asking for upgrades?'

'Sir, we can only store footage for up to 31 days. After that, we have to delete the old footage and record it. This is getting painful. It is also bad from a security perspective.'

'Arre, Siyaam, don't worry. We can store footage for 31 days, no? That is good enough. Let's try to get the CCTV camera repaired. I don't know if the trustees will allocate money even for that, but I'll talk to them. I will let you know.'

Ghulam wondered how the security could be so lax. The curator didn't seem to care that visitors near his office would be able to hear him. The guard was outside the room where the artefacts were on display and couldn't see him at all.

As if reading his thoughts, the guard, who had been snoozing outside in the corridor, belched and got up from his chair, which made a scraping sound. Then, he entered the hall in which Ghulam was standing and listening to the conversation between the curator and Siyaam. Not wanting to arouse the guard's suspicion, Ghulam quickly exited the museum. From the grounds, he carefully studied the architecture of the building. From the outside, he could clearly see the terrace. *The ventilators must be located on that terrace*, he thought excitedly. He took out his mobile and was about to click a picture when a more alert guard, who was now patrolling the grounds, came over to Ghulam and asked sharply, 'What are you doing?'

Ghulam was a quick thinker. He said, 'I'm taking a selfie.'

The guard said curtly, 'Photography not allowed,' pointing to a sign that was written in English and Urdu. Ghulam shrugged and putting the phone back in his pocket, he quickly walked out. He was afraid that the guard might demand to see if he had taken more photos inside the museum.

After exiting the museum quickly, he stopped in the small lane outside. The building housing the museum was visible from outside the boundary wall of the Purani Haveli, out of sight of the security guards. So, Ghulam stopped to study the architecture of the building carefully. He could make out two terraces. One terrace was directly above the corridor and there was another, which had to be above the halls displaying the precious artefacts. He guessed that the ventilator must be located on the walls joining the lower and upper terrace. He looked around carefully. He was in a lane that was not used much. Nobody noticed him. He took a few photos of parts of the museum that were visible from the lane.

That evening, he met Badshah at his house and showed him the photos.

'*Wah wah. Ekdam kirak* (Wow, what great photos)! My God, so much gold! I would feel like a *badshah* (king) just holding these in my hands,' Badshah said. The sight of the gold artefacts and thoughts of easy money brought out the poet in him.

'You can feel like a badshah after the deed. Now, let's think of a foolproof plan to steal these. I don't want to go to jail,' Ghulam said.

The Nizam's Museum; the terrace through which the thieves entered can be clearly seen

Source: The Hyderabad Police

'Arre bhai, there is no need to be afraid of jails. I have been to jail so many times. It's nothing.'

'So you want to go to jail after stealing these, or do you want to roam free as a rich man?' Ghulam asked a trifle curtly.

'You pain in the ass, don't mess around with me, else I will slap you!' Badshah said, glaring at Ghulam and raising his hand threateningly.

Ghulam, who was wary of Badshah's short temper and foul mouth, immediately adopted a contrite tone. 'I want the same thing as you, Ustaad! Sorry if you felt bad.'

Badshah nodded curtly to show that he accepted the apology. 'See, talk with respect and you will be respected,' he said sulkily.

Ghulam inclined his head. Then, in a more respectful tone, he said, 'Let's go in after two weeks and see what the best route to enter the museum is. I'll also take you inside the museum. You can see the beautiful items there first-hand. There are lots of CCTV cameras on the main roads. So, we have to use the by-lanes to avoid detection. We'll also check out all the by-lanes.'

'Yes, good idea, bhai,' Badshah said, his good humour restored by Ghulam's tone.

'After the theft, we'll take these by-lanes not only to avoid detection but also to make the police think that we are locals. Because, after all, only the locals will know all the lanes, won't they? But why can't we go tomorrow?' Badshah asked, dabbing his perspiring face with a pristine white handkerchief.

Ghulam shook his head sagely. 'It'll be safer to wait for a few days. I've gone to that area twice already in the past four days. People might remember my face. Let's wait for some time before going back. Please trust me, Ustaad.'

Badshah sighed in frustration. 'Okay. Then I'll need to do a house burglary in between. I need the money. I can see that as per your plan, we won't be able to carry out the actual theft for at least two to three months from now.'

'Can I come with you, Ustaad? I, too, need money. My wife is six months pregnant now. I need to take her to the doctor and I also need to see a doctor,' Ghulam asked humbly.

'You have still not recovered fully from your accident?' Badshah asked.

'No, Ustaad. I still get a lot of headaches and feel numbness in my arms.'

'Okay, tomorrow we'll rob a house in Telecom Nagar. I did the construction work on that house. The owner is super-rich and an asshole. He always tries to underpay his workers. Both husband and wife work and don't have kids. Currently, they're on vacation. It will be easy to rob their house.'

'How do you know they are on vacation?'

'Arre, their *kaamwali bai* (domestic worker) is a good friend of mine! *Potti* (sexy)! She is in love with me, but there are so many girls!' Badshah said, winking.

'Does she know that you are married?' Ghulam asked dryly.

'She thinks that I am going to marry her. I am stringing her along. She's strictly a use-and-throw item,' Badshah said with a smirk.

The next night they burgled the house without any trouble. They only found a few gold bangles and chains and didn't get as much money as they had anticipated. Badshah magnanimously gave a major part of the loot to Ghulam. Though he didn't admit it openly, he had realized that Ghulam was more intelligent than him, and he needed a brainy person as an assistant. Over the fortnight, they burgled three more houses to sustain themselves.

After two weeks, they went back to the Old City on Ghulam's bike to find the best way to get inside the museum and to check for cameras. Ghulam had insisted that Badshah should wear less flashy clothes than normal. So, they wore white kurta pyjamas, crocheted hats and lined their eyes with kohl to blend in with the crowd. They recced the road leading to the hospital and the museum. There was a lane leading away from the museum. It was so narrow that only a bike could pass through. They took this lane and reached another narrow lane, which housed several residences and a stationery shop. They came out of the lane and reached the main road again. There were several shops on both sides of the road selling clothes, medicines, water and so on. Then, there was a roundabout. A foul-smelling drain divided the road next to the roundabout. They took this road and reached the Mata-ki-Khidki temple. They followed the narrow lane.

'Look, this apartment building has a CCTV camera,' Ghulam, who had sharp eyes, told Badshah as he inspected the building. We cannot possibly take this road. Anyway, let's see where it leads.' They went further in, and they saw a masjid at the end of a small lane, leading from the main road.

'Look, another CCTV camera on the top of the masjid,' Ghulam said.

'Yes, but look at that house next to the masjid at that corner. It is closest to the museum.'

They parked their bikes nearby and went into the white, lime-washed house next to the masjid. The small lane leading to the masjid sharply turned and continued to snake from this house to another tiny one- or two-floor houses, all abutting each other without any gaps in between. This was the small lane parallel to the main road. They took that lane and reached the main road again, near the Mata-ki-Khidki temple close to the roundabout. They decided to go back to Rajendra Nagar for the day and come back another day in the early morning to see if they could get inside the house next to the masjid undetected.

Two days later, they woke up at 3.00 a.m. and reached the Mata-ki-Khidki temple around 3.30 a.m. Several empty autos were parked along the road for the night. That day, they wore dark pathani clothes. They parked their bike close to the autos under a mango tree and walked through the side lane, reaching the masjid in about 30 minutes at nearly 4.00 a.m. The sky was lightening and the visibility improved. Nobody was around. They quickly unlocked the gate of the building adjacent to the masjid and went in. Nobody stopped them. The whole world seemed to be asleep. They switched on a tiny torch and climbed the dark staircase. They reached the terrace on the second floor of the residential building, whose wall abutted the wall of the museum. They switched off the torch as the sun rose. They went to the far end of the terrace. There was a low boundary wall which separated this terrace from the roof of the Mukarram Jah School. There were no guards on duty at that hour. The two men jumped onto the terrace of the school. There was an iron ladder that led to the roof directly over the halls of the museum. They climbed up the ladder.

'This must be the main roof. The halls below have the precious artefacts,' Ghulam told Badshah in a low voice. He went to the side of the terrace and looked down onto another lower roof. 'This is the roof over the corridor,' he told Badshah excitedly. They jumped down lightly onto this terrace. They could see the row of ventilators now. 'We will need to break open the ventilator. Then, we will be inside the room. We will need a rope. This is a very high-ceilinged room. It will not be possible to climb down without a rope.'

'But there are so many ventilators. Which one is closest to the tiffin box?' Badshah asked Ghulam.

'Hmm, good point. Let me think,' Ghulam said as he looked over the wall to the grounds below. 'We will need to get out soon. It is getting brighter,' he added nervously.

Badshah, on the other hand, was icy calm. 'Nothing will happen. We still have around 15 minutes in hand before it is light. Think with a cool mind,' he urged Ghulam.

'Okay, okay,' Ghulam said, wiping his forehead. He was sweating despite the cool morning. Then, he spotted the dried trees. 'Okay, I know which ventilator is the closest,' he told Badshah. 'This ventilator is directly opposite that dried tree,' he said, pointing to it.

Badshah took out a chisel and marked an arrow above the ventilator. 'We need to move fast now,' he muttered.

They quickly climbed back onto the higher terrace, where Badshah drew another arrow with the chisel that he had brought with him. 'This is the place we will jump down to. It leads directly to the ventilator that we will need to break.' As they moved along, Badshah quickly drew a star leading to the second arrow that he had already drawn. 'Now, there will be no confusion,' he said in a satisfied voice.

'Yes, Ustaad,' Ghulam said, wiping his sweaty face with a dirty handkerchief. 'Good thinking, otherwise, it is quite possible that we will get totally confused in the dark,' he added in an oily voice.

'Yes, now, let's quickly get the hell out of here,' Badshah said. As they walked back to where they had parked their bike, the azaan in the masjid started. Ghulam looked at the time on his mobile. It was 5.15 a.m. and the sky had already lightened. That evening, they met again at Ghulam's house. His wife had gone to a friend's house.

'Ustaad, I have been thinking. We can't commit the theft from the house adjacent to the masjid. There are two to three CCTV cameras in that lane, from Mata-ki-Khidki temple to the masjid. Our images will be captured. We have to find some other way. Let's go tomorrow and see if we can find another way.'

'Ghulam, bhai, I can't wake up every day at 3.00 a.m. for you. It's sheer torture. I have a headache even now,' Badshah said clutching his head in despair.

'Arre nahi, Ustaad. Tomorrow, we will go there around 11.00 a.m. like *sharif* (decent) folks. Don't you worry,' Ghulam said with a chuckle.

A second arrow mark made by the thieves to mark the ventilator they would break to enter the museum

Source: The Hyderabad Police

The masjid next to the museum. CCTV footage from this masjid captured the thieves wearing masks getting away on their bike. The house beside it was the one used by the thieves to enter the museum.

Source: The Hyderabad Police

The next day, they returned to the Old City and just before turning towards the hospital, Ghulam noted a newly painted apartment on the main road. Razvi Tiffin Centre was located on the ground floor of the building, and besides that, a retail store. A staircase from the tiffin centre led to the floors above. Badshah and Ghulam parked their bike and went up the stairs. Nobody stopped them. There were several apartments on the first floor. Most of the doors were open but had screens. They could hear the voices of men, women and children. Careful not to be audible, the two men went to the terrace on the second floor. From there, they could see The Nizam's Museum. Typical of the Old City, there were no spaces between consecutive houses. They could easily move from one terrace to the next and reach the house adjacent to the masjid, which they had recced two days before. They came down as nonchalantly as they had gone up. Again, nobody stopped or questioned them.

As they sped away, Ghulam spotted Pista House and said, '*Arre, zara kuch khilao, Ustaad* (Give me a treat, Ustaad)!'

'*Pinde ki meri! Kaam bole to nakko terku lekin phukat ka khana hona* (You are always asking for free treats)!' Badshah chided affectionately as he stopped the bike. He treated Ghulam to pastries and bought a packet of the famous Osmania biscuits to take home to his wife.

They met again the next day to further discuss the plan. 'We'll try to reach the house adjacent to the museum from the house where the tiffin centre is located, as there are too many CCTV cameras on the road next to the Mata-ki-Khidki temple,' Ghulam said.

'Okay, so should we commit the theft day after tomorrow?' Badshah asked eagerly.

'*Pagal hai kya, Ustaad* (Are you crazy, Ustaad)! We have been captured by CCTV cameras in various places while recceing the area. We'll need to wait at least 40 days before committing the theft.'

'Why do we need to wait for 40 days? You are too cautious,' Badshah commented surlily.

Ghulam folded his hand and said, 'Ustaad, the CCTV footage in the museum gets deleted every 30 days. To be on the safe side, we should wait 40 days. The moment the theft happens, the police will scan the footage from every CCTV camera in that area. We are outsiders, and we have gone so many times to that area. The police will instantly be suspicious, and they know all about you! So, we need to be particularly cautious. Please be patient.'

'How do you know that the CCTV footage gets deleted every 30 days?' Badshah asked suspiciously.

'Bhai, I overheard the CCTV technician say this to one saab sitting in the museum office when I visited the museum the other day. It is authentic information, don't worry.'

'*Thik hai, thik hai* (Okay, okay). And on the day of the theft, we'll need to wear face masks and gloves,' Badshah said craftily. He didn't want Ghulam to feel that he was doing all the planning alone.

Ghulam nodded. 'Yes, and we should take an extra pair of shirts. Immediately after the job is done, we should wear those shirts over our t-shirts. That way, if we are caught on camera while going to the museum, the police won't think that we are the same people in case we are captured on camera again while escaping! And...' Ghulam hesitated.

'Tell me,' Badshah said impatiently.

'I...I think we should tonsure our heads,' Ghulam said nervously.

'*Baigan ke baatan mat kar* (Don't say nonsensical things)! I am not getting my head tonsured for anybody,' Badshah said, running his hand through his hair. Badshah was a rather vain man, and he was proud of his full head of silky hair, which drew women to him.

'Ustaad, it's important. Please heed my advice. It'll regrow, and you'll enjoy in Dubai, and your wallet will be full of money.'

'Hmm...I'll think about it,' Badshah said, understanding the importance of tonsuring his hair, but he was still finding it difficult to make the sacrifice.

'Also, I'll take a mobile and allow myself to be recorded as if I am speaking to someone on the cell phone on the CCTV.'

'*Arre chutiye*! Are you mad? The police will trace you immediately!' Badshah said, waving his hand derogatorily.

'Let me finish, Ustaad. I said I would be captured in the CCTV footage using the phone. So, the police will suspect everybody who used their phones in that locality. But, my phone will have no SIM card. This way, we will divert the suspicion of the police.'

'*Kya kirak idea bola re tu* (This is an awesome idea)! This is bloody brilliant. We will also remove the number plates from our bike,' Badshah said slapping Ghulam on the back, rather hard. Ghulam winced, but he was happy with Badshah's praise.

'Yes, Ustaad, that will be good. So, let us wait for at least 40 days.'

Badshah took out his smartphone and opened the calendar. 'Okay, let me see, we will carry out the theft on the eve between 2 and 3 September.'

'Yes, Ustaad. During this time, I will practice some rope climbing so that I can easily climb down the ventilator with the help of a rope.'

'That is no big deal. In Prasad's Imax theatre, there is an area where people do rope climbing. Both of us will go and practise for a few days. I'll pay,' Badshah said, waving his hand magnanimously.

'Thanks, but assuming that we can take the gold items without any problems, how will we dispose of them?' Ghulam asked.

'First thing, we should get out of Hyderabad with the gold items. I've heard that we can get good buyers in Mumbai. I also have a good friend in Mumbai's Kamathipura area. He will help us. He has many prostitutes who he controls,' Badshah said, with a wink.

'That's lovely, Ustaad,' Ghulam said, mechanically. Right now, he was so tense that his feelings were numbed. There was a pause as Ghulam thought some more. Then, he said, 'We'll travel to Karnataka first. After spending time there, we will travel to Mumbai. This should be enough to confuse the police, I guess.'

Badshah nodded. He felt none of Ghulam's tension and thought that he was being over-cautious. But he wanted to keep Ghulam happy. 'Fine. Also, you had mentioned earlier that in the Saudi market, these artefacts will fetch more money. Do you have any contacts in Saudi who would be interested in buying this stuff?'

'I will try, Ustaad. Let's pray that this thing works out well,' Ghulam said.

9

THE ROBBERY AND ESCAPE

The day that Badshah and Ghulam had been plotting for had finally arrived—it was 2 September 2018. That night, Badshah stayed with Ghulam—both of them had a light dinner and slept off early.

Zeenat, Ghulam's wife, suspected that something was amiss. She held his hand and pulled him aside, where Badshah couldn't hear them and whispered despairingly, 'Ghulam, I don't know what you both have planned, but whatever you are doing is wrong.'

'I am telling you! We are not planning anything!' Ghulam snapped at her, shaking her hands off him.

'Oh yes? Then why did both of you tonsure your heads today? Ghulam, don't do it, please. I beg of you. The consequences will be really bad. I have a very bad feeling about this, and you are not even telling me where you are going,' she appealed to him.

Finally, Ghulam lied to Zeenat that Badshah and he were going to a construction site to work for a few days and they would be back soon. When Zeenat tried to reason with him again when they went to bed, he simply turned to the other side and pretended to snore. He was unstoppable. Truth be told, he, too, was not sure if he was doing the right thing. But, from the few other burglaries that he had committed with Badshah, Ghulam knew that Badshah was a pro. They hadn't been caught so far. They also practised rope climbing. He had some confidence that they would be able to pull it off. After all, there is no gain if there was no risk. He was tired of being poor, and he knew no other way of making money.

After Zeenat had fallen asleep, Ghulam stealthily got up and rechecked the duffle bag that Badshah would be carrying. It contained three screwdrivers of various sizes, a cutting plier, a nail puller, 10 hacksaw blades and a rope. Ghulam and Badshah had spent the previous day tying about 30 knots all over the rope for better grip. Ghulam also checked to make sure that the side pocket of the bag contained the hand gloves and masks they had bought the previous day to avoid identification. The other side pocket held the shirts they were planning to wear after the theft.

Adrenaline pumping through his body, he changed into dark jeans and a black t-shirt and checked that the pocket of the jeans had the cell phone without a SIM card. They would use the torch of the phone. He looked at Badshah, who was sleeping peacefully on the broken sofa. Admiring his friend's lack of fear, Ghulam shook Badshah awake.

A few minutes later, at 2.00 a.m., Badshah and Ghulam stealthily left the latter's home. Normally, this was the time they went to bed. But, today, sleep was far from their minds. The biggest journey of their lives was about to begin.

It was raining but not too heavily. Badshah's motorcycle, parked close to the wall outside their house, was wet. They had removed the number plates. They didn't start the engine, as the noise would awaken their neighbours. Ghulam thanked his stars that his new chawl was closer to the main road. His previous tenement had been close to that of his father's friend, who was a rather nosy guy.

They walked the motorcycle along the alley to the Rajendra Nagar main road, where Badshah fired the engine and they sped away. Their destination? The Nizam's Museum, Purani Haveli, where the biggest art heist in the recent history of Hyderabad was about to take place.

It took Badshah and Ghulam exactly half an hour to reach the building, where they had decided to park their bike. They went to the terrace of the building, and, from there, they had planned to jump from one building to the next until they reached the museum. But, as soon as they parked the bike, they were shocked to hear a voice asking querulously, 'What do you want? Why are you parking your bike here?' an old security guard peered at them in the semi-darkness with rheumy eyes. When they had recced the building before, nobody had objected to their parking.

'Who the hell is this madarchod?' Badshah hissed in a furious, low tone. He did not like the fact the theft was not going as per plan.

Ghulam, a milder and more mature person, said nervously, 'Don't pick a fight now. He might recognize you later! Let's get away from here. Luckily, the lights here are dim.'

'What will we do now? Should we abort?' Badshah asked as they sped away from the building.

'No, we will complete this today, whatever happens,' Ghulam said in a determined voice. 'Let's take the small lane by the masjid that we took the other day. We'll park the bike near the masjid and walk the rest of the way.' So, they went to the roundabout near the sewage canal.

'Stop here. Let us wear our masks. There are too many CCTV cameras in that lane,' Ghulam said in a low voice. So, they stopped and wore their masks and gloves. Ghulam was quite satisfied that nobody would be able to recognize them even if they were caught on camera.

Soon, they reached the masjid and parked their bike. It was 2.45 a.m. and the world was in deep sleep. The only witness to their presence was a CCTV camera fitted to the wall of the mosque. Ghulam took out his phone without the card and pretended to use it.

Grabbing the duffle bags they had brought with them, Badshah and Ghulam walked swiftly, despite the total darkness, to the house adjacent to the museum. The gate was unlocked. Having surveyed the house before, they were not bothered by the darkness. Switching on the torch of the SIM-less mobile phone, they went up the staircase to the terrace and then jumped to the terrace of the museum. Nobody heard the slight thump they made. They grinned at each other in excitement. They were on their way to becoming rich.

They reached the roof of the museum and found the right ventilator easily, thanks to the arrow marks Badshah had made on the parapet wall. Badshah and Ghulam carefully removed the ventilator with the tools they had carried. They made very little noise. They had decided that Ghulam, who was slimmer than Badshah, would go down the ventilator. Badshah tied one end of the rope to the parapet wall and the other end to Ghulam's waist and lowered him slowly into the museum hall through the ventilator. He looked at the time on his phone. It was already 3.20 a.m. and getting lighter. They should have started earlier, he thought regretfully.

Ghulam quickly grabbed the artefacts and Badshah pulled him back onto the terrace.

Ensuring that their masks had not slipped from their faces, they rushed back to their parked bike. The sun was up by this time. Ghulam pretended to talk on his cell phone again while Badshah started the bike. Then, he got on the bike, and they sped away with gold worth crores of rupees in their old and dusty duffle bags.

'*Mubarak ho, bhai* (Congratulations, bro)!' Badshah said, merrily waving his hand victoriously. 'Now we can live like badshahs.'

'Careful!' Ghulam said as the motorcycle wobbled. '*Picture abhi baki hai, Ustaad* (There is still a lot of work to be done),' Ghulam said. 'Take the lane next to the toy shop. We'll reach the gully of the museum. That's a quiet corner. There, we will remove our masks and gloves and also change our shirts.'

'Yes, good idea,' Badshah said, chortling merrily.

After that, to avoid being tracked by the police via CCTV cameras, they avoided main roads and drove at random, taking by-lanes whenever they could. Finally, they reached Muthangi of Sangareddy district. A mild drizzle had started. They parked the bike and entered a small café.

'I am feeling tired and hungry now,' Badshah said with a loud yawn. He put a huge piece of dosa in his mouth and started chewing.

Ghulam, who was feeling sick with nervousness and tiredness was unable to eat and pushed his food around on his plate and said, 'Ustaad, we have come so far. We need to remain calm.'

Badshah laughed. 'Bhai, I'm calm. You look out for yourself.'

Ghulam nervously dabbed his sweaty face with his handkerchief. 'Though we have avoided the main roads as far as possible, I think we might have been captured by the cameras at some point or other. Like, near Mehdipatnam, and God knows where else,' he said nervously.

'True, Bhai,' Badshah chortled, 'but they will think that we are going out of Hyderabad and this will again work to our advantage. From here, let us take the service road and go back to Hyderabad.'

Ghulam smiled. He liked Badshah's idea. 'Yes, that sounds like a good plan. Let's take the service road along the outer ring road and go back to our home in Rajendra Nagar.'

There was a dairy farm in Rajendra Nagar, which was located in an isolated spot. As they neared it, Ghulam had a brainwave.

'Let's bury the bag in the field near the dairy farm,' he told Badshah excitedly. 'I know this area well. Nobody will come to this jungle.'

So, they went to a nearby land full of trees and weeds. While Ghulam kept a lookout, Badshah, the stronger one of the two, quickly dug a pit and buried the bag with their loot in it.

'Tomorrow, if all goes well, we will dig up the bag and go to Mumbai on our bike to dispose of the gold as planned,' Ghulam said.

Badshah nodded, wiping his hands with a rag that he kept on Ghulam's bike, perspiring heavily. Digging was hard work and he was becoming soft.

They went back to Badshah's home. Ghulam quickly switched on the television. News of the theft was already on the news. They flipped through the news channels. All of them were covering the theft at The Nizam's Museum. Ghulam felt dizzy. The enormity of his crime finally struck him in full and he started to shake.

'Arre bhai, why are you afraid?' Badshah reprimanded him. 'Finally, we have handled a big crime and that too successfully. Now, I'll go and spit on my father's face. He told me that if I have to be a criminal, I should at least score something that would count as a big crime. I wonder what he will have to say now! *Saala chutiya*! Come now, let's celebrate.'

All Badshah wanted to do was visit prostitutes, have sex and have a good time, but Ghulam was too scared and continued to look over his shoulders.

Finally, Badshah got fed up, went out and bought some biryani and alcohol and spent the rest of the day watching the news, eating and drinking. As the news spread like wildfire, Badshah became increasingly cocky while Ghulam became jumpier. In fact, the smell of the beef biryani and alcohol, made him feel nauseous. Finally, Badshah got irritated.

'Arre bhai! How many times should I tell you? There is nothing to worry about. The police can never catch us,' he extended his alcohol bottle towards Ghulam and said, 'here, drink some alcohol. It'll calm you down. Now, compose yourself. If you are so tense, people will start suspecting something.'

But Ghulam wouldn't drink. So, finally, Badshah forced some alcohol down his throat, which Ghulam immediately vomited out. The smell of vomit sickened Badshah and leaving Ghulam to clean up the mess, he went out to visit his favourite prostitute.

By the next morning, when the police didn't come banging on his door at night as he had feared, Ghulam regained some of his courage. After a quick snack, they dug up the stolen bag.

Then, they took the same service road and reached Zaheerabad.

Badshah was feeling hungry. 'Let's have lunch here,' he said. Ghulam didn't want to stop, but he knew that Badshah would become very aggressive if he continued to remain hungry so he agreed. After having biryani, when Badshah tried to restart the bike, it wouldn't start.

'What should we do now, Ustaad?' Ghulam asked nervously. Though he had calmed down since the last day, he was still extremely nervous.

'Let's abandon the bike here. We'll take a bus to Karnataka. From there, we can take another bus to Mumbai,' Badshah said after thinking for a minute.

On the bus, Ghulam said, 'Ustaad, what will happen to the bike now?'

'*Baigaan ke bataan mat kar* (Don't talk like a dickhead)! We will soon have crores of rupees and you are worried about a ₹30,000 bike. We'll buy new phones and SIM cards when we reach Karnataka. We'll use those to contact potential buyers.'

'What if the police trace the bike to us?' Ghulam asked, anxiously scratching his arms and looking around as if he expected the police to jump out at any moment.

'Bhai, how will they connect a bike in Zaheerabad to a theft in Old City? Do you think the police are that smart? In that case, I would have had to shut my business long back. I keep telling you, stop being so nervous. You will attract more attention. Just behave normally and confidently like me. Let's go!' Badshah slung the bag over his shoulder and walked confidently to the bus stop.

They spent the night in a seedy hotel in Karnataka and then took a bus from Palar in Karnataka to Mumbai. When they reached the outskirts of Mumbai, they heaved a sigh of relief.

They would be more difficult to trace in a big city like Mumbai. It was past 7.30 p.m. when they reached Dadar and were met by Badshah's friend Ashraf, who was a petty thief and a pimp working in Kamathipura, a red-light district in South Mumbai. He had booked a room for Badshah and Ghulam at a guest house where one could rent rooms by the hour, no questions asked. Ashraf knew the owner well and got them the room at a discounted rate.

After helping them settle down, Ashraf left, promising to come back the next morning. Ashraf was aware that they were in Mumbai to sell some gold. Badshah had promised to pay him ₹10,000 once the gold was sold, but Ashraf didn't know that they were trying to sell the artefacts from The Nizam's Museum. He didn't even know of the theft, as he didn't read newspapers or, for that matter, anything, because he was illiterate. In any case, he was least interested in news and such, spending most of his waking hours in a haze of drugs and alcohol.

That evening, Ghulam and Badshah ordered some biryani from a small restaurant. After bringing the biryani back to their guest house, Badshah took out the tiffin box and cup. He lovingly wiped it with a clean cloth. He turned the box around in the light—the diamonds sparkled and the gold glittered, taking his breath away. Ghulam, who had regained some of his confidence after arriving in Mumbai, watched Badshah's antics in amusement. Badshah took the silver foil bag containing the biryani, cut it open and emptied it into the gold box. He poured the accompanying raita into the gold cup and arranged the onion rings on the gold saucer. The mouth-watering aroma of biryani, wafting out of the sparkling gold tiffin box, filled the room. They felt like kings, despite the seediness of the room.

He and Ghulam, then sat down to eat. 'Today onwards, we'll eat from this box and drink from this cup till we are able to find a buyer. I really want to feel like a badshah.'

The next morning, Ghulam said, 'Today onwards, we will focus on trying to sell the items Ustaad, enough of this *mauj masti.*'

Badshah nodded, albeit reluctantly. Sensing Badshah's reluctance, Ghulam emphasized, 'We need to be very careful, Ustaad. At the rate that we are spending, our money won't last long.'

They had a plate of vada pav at a nearby eatery and feeling satiated, came back to their room and waited for Ashraf to show up.

'In this big city, if the wrong kind of people come to know about our loot, they might rob us!' Ghulam said nervously.

Badshah scoffed, '*Arre dar nako* (Don't be afraid)! I'm with you. I'm also quite dangerous, don't worry.'

'We'll not show the actual tiffin to the buyers. We'll take some good photos of the items on your phone. We'll show the photos to the buyers initially.'

'Where'll we hide the tiffin and the cup, saucer and spoon when we go out to meet the buyers?' Badshah asked.

Ghulam thought for some time. It would be too risky to hide the artefacts in their room.

Finally, he said, 'We will carry them in our backpack. But we won't take them out till the deal is finalized,' he suggested. Badshah nodded approvingly. He thought that this was a good idea. This Ghulam was turning out to be quite useful and intelligent, he thought to himself.

'How much should we sell them for?' Badshah asked, after a pause.

Ghulam nodded sagely. He had been thinking about it. 'Ustaad, in the international market these kinds of items would sell for several crores. We should ask for at least one crore.'

Badshah nodded his head appreciatively, 'Yes, you are right. We won't settle for anything less than a crore.'

'What if the buyer realizes that these are the artefacts stolen from The Nizam's Museum and reports us to the police?' Ghulam asked.

'Bhai, don't overthink. You will unnecessarily get tense and make me tense as well. We will cross that bridge when we come to it,' Badshah said. 'Remember, *jo dar gaya, woh mar gaya* (A person who gets afraid, will definitely die)!' he added.

∽

It was 1.00 p.m. by the time Ashraf came to their guest house.

'*Miyaan* (dude), you were supposed to come by 11.00 a.m.,' Badshah grumbled.

'Chill, dude. Nobody starts working before noon in the area where I am taking you,' Ashraf said, patronizingly. He thought of Ghulam and Badshah as stupid small-time criminals.

After stepping out, they took a kali-peeli[22]. 'Chira Bazaar,' Ashraf told the taxi driver.

They got down near the Chira Bazaar bus stop and started walking down the road. It was a rather seedy looking place with a lot of very old buildings that badly needed repair and a coat of paint.

Where are we going? Ghulam thought to himself. He had expected Ashraf to take them to some rich man's house. Instead, they were in this dirty-looking place. He felt slightly

---

[22]Black and yellow taxi commonly found in Mumbai

more at ease when he saw a row of gold shops looming in the distance as they walked on.

Ashraf led them to a rather sleazy looking, narrow and tiny gold shop. Most of the space available was filled with display units in which bangles, necklaces and other items were displayed. There was a brass idol of Ganesha, decorated with fragrant jasmine flowers. The shop smelled strongly of incense.

A rather sour-looking shrivelled old man was sitting behind the cash counter and a younger man was lounging next to him, looking bored. There were no customers in the shop.

Ashraf went to the man and whispered something in his ear. The man looked up and stared at Badshah and Ghulam appraisingly. Then, he invited them into a small room at the back of the shop. The room had a mattress covered with a white sheet and pillows covered with white pillowcases. There were pictures of various gods and goddesses on the wall and a big, old-fashioned safe stood in the corner of the room. An air-conditioner ran rather noisily.

'Show me what gold you have,' the man said. He had a thin monotonous voice with a strong Gujarati accent.

'We haven't brought the items with us,' Badshah told him roughly. 'We'll show you the pictures. If we finalize a rate, we'll deliver the goods and take the cash at the same time.'

'But I won't be able to tell you a price unless I have seen the items,' the man said testily.

'Well, right now we don't have the items,' Ghulam said softly, 'but we can show you the pictures.'

'Okay, show me the pictures then.'

After seeing the pictures of the gold tiffin box, the cup, saucer and spoon, the man said, 'I will pay a maximum of ₹5 lakh for these.'

'What! ₹5 lakh only! The box itself weighs around 5 kg,' Badshah said, snorting in disgust.

The man remained unmoved. He looked coldly at Badshah and said testily, 'Look, dude, I'll take the box, melt it and make new jewellery. There'll be a lot of waste. This is the best I can give. If you show me the actual item, I may increase my offer. But, right now, I'll give a maximum amount of ₹5 lakh. Take it or leave it.'

They walked out of the shop extremely disappointed. 'What kind of cheap shop have you brought us to?' Badshah snarled at Ashraf.

'This is the best I can do. Why don't you try to find a buyer yourself? You are trying to sell 5 kg of gold, yet you will pay me only ₹10,000!' Ashraf growled back.

'Calm down, you two! Don't fight here. We'll come under the radar of the police,' Ghulam said in a low voice. He turned to Ashraf and said, 'We will pay you more. But first, let us find a buyer. Maybe you can take us to some other shop?'

Ashraf calmed down a little. 'I'll take you to another shop, but don't expect a better deal,' he said grudgingly.

As predicted by Ashraf, the owner of the second gold shop, another seedy place, said, 'You bring the items and keep them with me. I'll melt and resell them, and I will pay you 50 per cent of my profit.'

'How much will that come to?' Ashraf asked.

'Well, probably around ₹20 lakh,' the man in the shop said confidently.

'Just ₹20 lakh?' Ghulam asked incredulously.

'There is at least 5 kg in gold and it is studded with diamonds,' Badshah added.

'I don't deal with diamonds. I can only give the price for

the gold and I assure you nobody will give a better price than me,' the owner said persuasively.

'So, we will need to leave the items with you and you will share the profit once you melt and resell the gold?' Badshah asked.

'Yes,' the man responded.

'And what is the guarantee that he will share the profit?' Badshah asked aggressively, turning towards Ashraf.

'You will have to trust me, bhaiyya. Otherwise, where will I get the money to give you?' the owner responded angrily.

Ghulam signalled to Badshah that they should leave. 'We shouldn't get into this business of leaving the gold with a man we don't even know,' he told Badshah and Ashraf after they walked out and put some distance between them and the store. Disheartened, they decided to try their luck again the next day.

That night, Badshah sat down with a screwdriver that they had bought from a local shop and pried off the diamonds. They decided they would sell the diamonds and the tiffin box separately.

But, the next day was no better. They decided to show the tiffin instead of the picture, as many of the jewellers did not take them seriously when they said they had gold items to sell because of their shabby appearance and cheap clothes. Then, they noticed that a man was following them at a distance. They got scared and returned to their rooms through a rather circuitous path. The man followed them for some time but dropped out of sight when he understood that they had seen him following them.

Badshah, Ashraf and Ghulam were so scared by this experience that they decided to lay low for a while. They spent the next day holed up in their room, getting their meals delivered to their room. They went out only once in the afternoon and bought a murderous-looking folding knife for self-protection.

The next day, Ashraf called them up. 'I have got a new contact in Chor Bazaar. I will come and pick you guys up by 1.00 p.m.'

They took another kali-peeli and had travelled for only five minutes when Ashraf asked the driver to stop near Grant Road railway station.

'We could have covered such a short distance on foot only! This was an unnecessary wastage of ₹100 when money is scarce,' Ghulam grumbled.

'We'll have to walk a lot inside the gully,' Ashraf, who never walked if he could help it, said, dabbing his sweaty face with a white handkerchief. 'In this humid weather, it'll be difficult.'

'*Behenchod*! You know that we are short of money. Yet you don't care a bit and spend our money like water,' Badshah growled.

'If you speak to me this way, I won't help you,' Ashraf snarled.

'You are asking for more money and yet, you can't get us a good buyer. Three days have already passed!' Badshah fumed, clenching his hands in anger.

'Calm down, calm down!' Ghulam said, pointing his hands to his chest, 'Now is not the time to fight. Ashraf bhai, don't pay any attention to Badshah. I am here, no?'

'And where have you got us?' asked Badshah looking around disdainfully. The area they were in had a number of narrow streets and crumbling buildings. Various vendors were selling fake Rolexes, cheap t-shirts, iPhones and other electronic gadgets.

Ghulam patted Badshah's hand and said, 'Bhai, be calm. Ashraf will take us to the correct place, just be patient.'

They left that lane behind and walked through another lane. This lane had a lot of shops all selling scrap items from bikes. The smell of garbage mingled with faint cooking smells from nearby buildings. There were rundown apartments above most of these shops. Washed clothes were drying on lines in most of the balconies. But the trio felt comfortable in these by-lanes, as it was a Muslim area. Many dismantled bikes were lying around in heaps on the roadside.

'What are these bikes?' Ghulam asked, bemused.

'Some are old bikes and some stolen,' Ashraf responded, tersely.

The streets were getting less crowded as they walked deeper into Chor Bazaar. The delicious smell of biryani wafted into their nostrils. It was coming from a restaurant tucked in among the shops. Badshah's stomach rumbled. They had had a late, meagre breakfast of vada pav again from the joint near their guest house and it was past 2.00 p.m. He felt hungry and missed his home food.

Ashraf was walking fast and they hurried to keep up with him. They turned into another lane, which was full of shops selling trinkets and other antique pieces. There was a shop selling musical instruments and another one selling real and fake old lamps.

Ashraf stopped in front of a shop named 'Old Is Gold'. An old Muslim man with a white beard, wearing a white kurta–pyjama and a white skull cap, was sitting in a plastic chair in front of the shop.

'As-salaam alaikum!' Ashraf greeted the man raising his hand towards his forehead.

'Walaikum as-salaam!' the man responded.

'We are looking for Shakeel bhai.'

'He's at the back of the store.' Obviously, the man had been expecting them.

He got up from the chair and flicked a switch. The dim shop lit up and they saw that it was a long shop, full of items on both sides, separated by a narrow aisle leading to the back of the shop. At the far end of the shop was a narrow alcove, and they could see that it led to another room.

As they followed the man to the back of the shop, Badshah and Ghulam felt like they were inside Aladdin's cave. The shop was full of statues, lamps, old clocks, gramophones, records and musical instruments. Badshah was sure that there would be items stolen from rich homes in Mumbai and other areas that had found their way into this shop.

They entered a biggish room beyond the alcove with green walls, some mismatched sofas and tables covered with lace tablecloths. An expensive-looking carpet covered the floor. The room was air-conditioned. A man in his early forties, dressed in a kurta-pyjama, was sitting in a rocking chair next to the sofas. He had a well-groomed beard and cold eyes lined with black kohl. The smell of attar wafted in the air.

Ashraf bowed to the man, 'As-salaam alaikum, Shakeel bhai,' he said, in a deferential voice. 'We have got something special for you.'

The man guided them to the nearest sofa with a lazy wave of his hands. 'Tell me, what have you got?' he asked in a curiously soft, whispering voice. Ghulam and Badshah somehow felt extremely scared of this man.

They instinctively knew that this guy Shakeel was way out of their league on the criminal ladder.

Ghulam said in a low, respectful tone, 'We have got the photos. If you like them, we'll get the items.'

The man stretched out his hand without a word. Badshah brought up the photos on his phone and handed it over to Shakeel.

'Hmm, where did you get these items? '

'From a rich man's house in Hyderabad,' Ghulam lied.

'Hmm…I'll need to see the items before I can quote a price.'

'Janaab, don't mind my asking, how will you pay us?' Ashraf asked, deferentially.

'I will pay cash. Don't worry about the money,' the man said.

'If you can tell us some approximate amount, Janaab,' Ghulam said hesitantly.

Shakeel looked at him appraisingly. Ghulam was reminded of a snake. A shiver ran down his spine.

'I told you, I need to see the item first. I'll get a gold expert tomorrow. You get the items and I'll tell you,' Shakeel said conclusively as he got up from his chair, clearly indicating that the conversation was over. 'Get the items first, then we'll talk again,' he repeated, dismissing them.

They walked back to the guest house in silence, ignoring Ashraf's grumbles.

After they returned to their room, Ghulam said, 'I didn't like this Shakeel. What if he grabs the items from us tomorrow and gives us nothing? He looks like a dangerous man to me. Ashraf bhai, how well do you know this Shakeel?'

'I don't know him that well, Bhai, but I heard that he has quite a few murders under his belt.'

'Both of you are such cowards,' Badshah said now. 'Bhai, my name is Khooni Badshah. Why are you afraid when I'm there?' he asked, producing the knife from his pocket, caressing the blade suggestively with his right hand.

'Bhai, this knife will be no match against his revolver,' Ashraf chortled.

'He carries a firearm?' Badshah asked in shock.

'They all do.'

'We won't go back tomorrow,' Ghulam said, shaking his head decisively.

Ashraf sighed in frustration. 'If you guys act like this, we'll never find any buyers. I don't know anybody else who may be willing to buy the items.'

'If we go back there with the items, that Shakeel will most probably take them away from us and probably murder us for good measure. I'm not going back there. I have a very bad feeling about that man,' Ghulam said decisively before turning to Ashraf and demanding, 'Where did you get his contact? Does he know where we are staying?'

'Don't worry so much,' Ashraf said curtly, 'you're safe enough here. This is my territory.' He was getting pissed off with their attitude. Ghulam and Badshah were also getting irritated with Ashraf.

The next day, they decided to try the shops in the Zaveri Bazaar on their own, but their luck turned for the worse at the very first shop. The owner of the shop exclaimed, 'Ah, this is the gold tiffin stolen from The Nizam's Museum! My nephew lives in Hyderabad. He was telling me about the theft.'

Ghulam and Badshah fled from the shop and hurried back to their room. Ghulam had contacted his friends in Saudi, but they, too, didn't seem interested in helping him find a buyer.

Ghulam and Badshah were starting to run out of money. As more people learnt that they had a lot of gold on them, they no longer felt that Mumbai was safe for them. They were also worried that the man at the gold shop in Zaveri Bazaar would alert the police. 'Let's go back to Hyderabad. We have more contacts there. Inshallah, we'll be able to find a buyer there,' Ghulam told Badshah.

With a heavy heart, they boarded a bus back to Hyderabad. All the dreams they had when they had stolen the gold seemed to be crashing around them. What good was the gold if they couldn't find a suitable buyer?

10

THE CHASE CONTINUES

The police were investigating the theft zealously, going all out to find the culprits. When the investigation had begun, hopes had been high, as many promising leads—like the CCTV footage, bike model and the facts that the thieves had been carrying a cell phone and had masonry expertise—had been discovered. However, now, quite some time had passed since the theft and almost all the leads had fizzled out. The Commissioner was worried that the artefacts had been smuggled out of India and would never be recovered. But he couldn't show his desperation and tried very hard to boost the morale of the team. The entire Hyderabad Police team was dispirited.

Initially, the entire list of blue Pulsar 200 NS models was checked. The details of some of the bikes were not available and the ownership of all the bikes could not be verified, much to the disappointment of the police. But, the image of the bike yielded rich dividends. All the known criminals in Hyderabad with this model of bike were checked out. The police were able to identify that one of the bikes belonged to a man called Ghulam. But he had no criminal record. So, the police had no clue about his involvement in the theft.

The team monitoring the thieves' entry and exit routes came up with better quality and colour footage as the days passed. The enhanced video footage was shared with all the police stations of Hyderabad, Cyberabad and Rachakonda, but the offenders had disappeared from the police's radar. They realized that the thieves must have taken the narrow lanes and by-lanes of the Old City colonies and avoided the main roads to evade the CCTVs. The process of tracing and sifting through the mounds of footage took several backbreaking days. The route taken by the thieves from the masjid in the Purani Haveli area was traced to Gachibowli. Although the actual distance between the two places was only 20 km, the police had to trace every possible route, from the Old City to the newer part of the city, gathering thousands of hours of footage along all possible routes. Despite the hard work, the tracks of the thieves were lost after Gachibowli. It was back-breaking and discouraging work.

Inspector Purna's team had continued with the task of gathering CCTV footage from all the shops that had cameras installed along all the possible paths that the thieves could have taken. Most of the shops and buildings cooperated and gave them the required data. The other teams of the detective department, in the meantime, continued the painstaking job of identifying the thieves in the footage. After hours of checking the CCTV footage, they could trace the exact path taken by the thieves, which looked like this:

The Nizam's Museum → Madina Junction → Purana Pul → Tappachabutra → Mehdipatnam → Shaikpet → Raidurgam → Gachibowli → Tellapur → Bharat Heavy Electricals Limited (BHEL) → Patancheruvu

The path was traced to Patancheruvu, around 3 km from Sangareddy, which has a major bus station for taking outstation buses. However, from there, the trace was lost. This led the police to believe that the thieves must have skipped town.

The team working on analysing the cell phone tower data dump, too, did not have a breakthrough. The tech team collected as many as 600 tower details (from 2,500 cell tower antennas). Then, they narrowed the list to 230 suspicious phone numbers. Based on this, about 200 people were questioned, but that too proved to be a dead end.[23]

Charminar and other surrounding areas are known for the sale of antique items during the weekends. As many as 50 traders and shopkeepers were questioned, but none of them could provide any significant leads. Verification of most of the recently released convicts and old property offenders, too, did not yield any result. All the ex-employees of the museum were questioned. The police even prepared a questionnaire for all the museum employees. This did not reveal any important clues either. Social media analysis also didn't yield any important information about the sale of antique items. However, Anjani Kumar, after reviewing the progress from time to time, appreciated the efforts and kept motivating the teams. His encouragement continued even when some teams didn't show the expected progress.

The media, both print and electronic, continued to focus on the theft. The sequence of events was narrated and rehashed, expert opinions were sought, and questions were raised about why the investigation was taking such a long time. The pressure

---

[23]After the capture, the police came to know that the cell phone was being used as a torch and had no SIM card. The thieves had tried to confound the police by leading them to believe that they could be traced via the cell phone.

was steadily mounting on the Hyderabad City Police to solve the case. As days passed without any major breakthrough, the police started to get a lot of negative press coverage. The media started openly criticizing the inability of the police to apprehend the perpetrators. The decision of the museum administrators to reopen the museum to visitors was also criticized.

'Keep Nizam's museum shut till security intensified, says expert,' *The New Indian Express* headline screamed. In the news report, Anuradha Naik, who was responsible for designing The Nizam's Museum, had said, 'Since there is a lapse in security, the other exhibits are still at risk. The conditions are still the same. Therefore, until better measures are taken to protect the remaining collection, they should be kept in a safe place. They should be protected, even if it means that the museum is closed to the public for a short period of time.'[24]

The heirs of the Nizam still share an emotional bond with the people of the Old City. Poor people visit the Durru Shehvar Hospital, which is a free hospital run by the Nizam's Trust. The trust also runs a girls' school and college in its vast building, at the same place where the museum is housed, shaping the career of young women from the Old City. Many poor and downtrodden families have benefited from the several charitable activities of the Nizam's Trust, which has helped their children progress and settle well in their respective lives. A gloom prevailed among these people upon learning about the stolen items. The poor folks staying in the seedy houses abutting the museum were also worried that they would be

---

[24]"Keep Nizam's Museum Shut Till Security Intensified, Says Expert', *The New Indian Express*, 9 September 2018, https://bit.ly/3S1cFBL. Accessed on 21 September 2022.

suspected of the theft. Many of them had criminal records and, thus, were under the police scanner.

The Commissioner continued to support and boost the morale of his team members, shielding them from the wrath of the higher authorities and personally fielding press hostility and comments. In his report to his superiors, he explained why the investigation was taking such a long time. He pointed out the following challenges faced by the police:

1. The museum theft was the first crime of its kind in Hyderabad. The only case study available was the theft at the Louvre Museum, an international theft committed over hundred years back.

2. The museum authorities did not maintain any record of visitors.

3. CCTV coverage in the museum was grossly inadequate. There were no high-quality cameras in the area. The number of CCTVs was also meagre. Only 31 days' footage was available. The police were sure that the criminals had recced the crime scene before the burglary, but had no evidence to prove this.

4. The routes leading to the museum had very few CCTVs.

5. No cell data record could be found, even though the police wasted countless man-hours trying to trace the cell phone. The tower dump analysis (about 600 towers) also yielded no results.

6. Internal differences between the two trusts of the Nizam's heirs raised the suspicion of the police. The insider angle needed to be ruled out. This was not an easy task.

7. No fingerprints were found at the scene of the crime. The criminals were smart enough to use hand gloves.

8. No incriminating material was found at the scene of the crime, except for the small arrows and the rope marks.

9. Due to the several houses abutting the museum, there were many ways to get inside it, making it difficult to identify the culprit's entry and exit routes.

10. The thieves tonsured their heads to avoid detection. They also wore face masks and changed shirts to avoid being spotted.

11. They also took various lanes and by-lanes of the city that did not have CCTVs, to avoid being traced. After Gachibowli, the police lost trace of the thieves.[25]

∽

While the police were trying their best to catch the culprits, Badshah and Ghulam had returned to Hyderabad, feeling bitter and disappointed.

'I think it was a mistake to grab the items from the museum without formulating a proper disposal plan,' Ghulam sighed. They were sitting in Ghulam's house.

'Madarchod, you are thinking about this now! We should have stuck to normal burglary! I thought you were smart, so I got persuaded by your half-baked plan!' Badshah accused Ghulam angrily.

'Ustaad, what can I do? I didn't know that my friends

---

[25]After their capture, the thieves confessed that they took the service road of the Outer Ring Road, which did not have CCTV cameras.

in Saudi wouldn't help me at all!' Ghulam said, wringing his hands despairingly.

'You have done enough!' Badshah told Ghulam roughly. 'Let me handle things from now.' He got up abruptly and went towards the main door.

Ghulam tried to stop him. 'Bhai...bhai, calm down. Where are you going? What are you planning to do?'

Badshah shoved him away roughly. 'Let me go! I will contact Sajid, my friend.'

Ghulam desperately held on to Badshah's arms, trying to prevent him from doing anything rash. 'Think before telling anybody, Ustaad. I have heard that he is a police informer.'

'Arre nahi...Sajid was in jail till a few months back. He is also a burglar, like me. He will have some contacts. Plus, he likes me! He will help. Let me go!' Badshah said, forcibly pulling his arm out of Ghulam's clutches. Ghulam didn't want Badshah to take such risky steps but he was unstoppable.

After coming out of Ghulam's home, Badshah called Sajid. 'As-salaam alaikum, I have a tiffin to sell.'

This call proved to be the final nail in the coffin for Badshah and Ghulam.

11

THE SCENT GETS STRONGER

Constable Idris was posted at the Mir Chowk PS. He took his job very seriously. He was proud of the fact that he had recently been selected to be a part of the Commissioner's Task Force and had to report to Inspector Madhu directly. Being smart and ambitious, he carefully maintained contacts with his network of criminals and informers, as he knew they could give him useful information that could help him rise up the ranks of the police force.

On 9 September 2018, Idris reported for duty at 8.00 a.m. sharp. He stepped out around 9.30 a.m. to have a cup of tea at the nearby tea stall. He had just taken the paper cup with the piping hot tea and was about to take a sip when his cell phone rang.

It was Sajid, one of his informants. '*Ustaad, khairiyat* (Bro, how are you)?' he asked.

'*Arre Sajid, hau ekdum kiraak! Aur tum batao* (Ah, Sajid! Yes, I am fine. You tell me),' Idris responded.

'I have some important information. But I need ₹2 lakh for this information.'

'*Lite le lo, miyaan! Hosh me to ho* (Take it easy brother! Are you in your senses)?'

'Ustaad, I am telling you, it is a big ticket item. It's about the tiffin.'

'Tiffin? What tiffin?'

'You tell me which tiffin could it be?'

Idris spilt the scalding hot tea on his hand in excitement and gasped in pain. 'Hold the line. I spilt tea on myself,' he said, grabbing the water bottle that the tea seller kept on the counter, he poured cold water on the affected area.

'Arre, don't waste my water!' the tea seller shouted.

'Can't you see? I have burnt my hand!' Idris retorted.

'So? Go to that tap over there!'

'*Madarchod, police ke muh pe jawab de raha hai! Andar karu kya tereku* (You motherfucker, you are answering back to the police! Should I put you in jail)?'

The tea seller stopped arguing. Idris pulled out his handkerchief and, wiping the affected area, continued the conversation. 'Somebody is trying to sell the tiffin box stolen from The Nizam's Museum?' he asked in a low voice.

'Yes,' Sajid said in a low voice.

'Who is it?' Idris said, lowering his voice.

'I will tell you only after I get my fee. Talk to someone senior in the police. I'll only talk after I get the cash. I can tell you the name of the thief and even help you to catch him.'

'How can you help catch him?'

'Because that person is asking my help for selling the tiffin box.'

'*Dekho Chiccha, baigan ke baataan nakko karo. Itna paisa police ke paas kaha se ayegi* (Look dude, don't talk gibberish. Where will the police get so much money from)?'

'I don't know and I don't care. If I get two ₹2 lakh, I'll tell you the name of the seller.'

'I'll discuss it with my boss and get back to you,' Idris promised.

He called Inspector Madhu, who was shaving when he took the call.

'Yes Idris, tell me,' he said putting his phone on speaker mode.

When Idris told him what Sajid had said, Madhu nearly cut himself in excitement. 'Are you sure it's the tiffin box from The Nizam's Museum?' he asked.

'Sajid says it is, Sir. But he says that he wants ₹2 lakh for the information,' Idris confirmed.

'Ask him where we can meet,' Inspector Madhu instructed.

Idris spoke to Sajid again and they agreed to meet at Bandlaguda near Chandrayangutta, a 30-minute drive from Mir Chowk. Then, he called Madhu with the update.

'Okay, you come over to my house. We'll go on my bike. I want to talk to him,' Madhu said.

'But ₹2 lakh, Sir!' Idris protested.

'We'll see. Come fast.'

After ending his call with Idris, Inspector Madhu called his boss, ACP Chaitanya and updated him. 'Should we pay him the money?' he asked.

'Let me talk to the Commissioner. I'll get back to you. But the information would better be correct. We don't want to be duped of ₹2 lakh by some conman,' Chaitanya said. He was a cautious person who rarely trusted anybody.

The ACP called the Commissioner and brought him up to speed about the events. The Commissioner immediately sanctioned the payment. ACP Chaitanya updated Madhu.

He had full freedom to pay up to ₹2 lakh in cash for the information.

As Idris started to walk towards the nearby auto stand, the tea stall owner yelled, 'Hey, give me my money!'

'I will give it to you tomorrow. Today, I need to go!' Idris called out.

'*Tum police walon ka koi bharosa nahin* (You police fellows are not trustworthy).'

'Hey! Don't talk nonsense, else I'll put you in jail!' Idris threatened before quickly taking a share auto to Madhu's home nearby. Madhu was waiting on the road outside his house with his bike when Idris arrived panting, having run from where the auto had dropped him near Madhu's home.

'Get on, get on,' Madhu said impatiently, firing up the bike.

They had been driving for 15 minutes when Idris's phone rang again. 'What! You can't meet in Bandlaguda! Then where do you want to meet?' Idris asked impatiently. Inspector Madhu slowed down.

Sajid said something over the phone. 'Bahadurpura Cross Road!' Idris exploded. 'Madarchod, we were right there. Now, we will have to turn back. Couldn't you have told me earlier?'

The voice at the other end said something placatory.

'Okay, okay, we're coming. Stay somewhere near the signal!'

Sajid, a tall dark man with a beard, dressed in a kurta-pyjama and a cap on his head, stood waiting for them close to the signal. Madhu knew Sajid, as he had to come regularly to the station for attendance. He had shifted to Rajendra Nagar and should have reported to the Rajendra Nagar PS, but his papers had not been transferred there, as he was not comfortable reporting to the PS over there. In lieu of this favour, he passed on titbits of information to Madhu and his team whenever he could, most of which used to be useless. Not this time, though. He saluted Madhu as the two men stopped the bike beside him.

'Idris told me that you have some information on the tiffin box stolen from The Nizam's Museum. Your information had better be correct. Otherwise, I'll turn your papers over to the Rajendra Nagar PS,' Madhu warned.

'Saab, stop threatening me all the time. I have the information. Have you got ₹2 lakh?'

'First, I will verify if what you say is correct; only then will I give you the money. How much depends on how good your information is,' Madhu said sternly.

'Saab, I need the money. My father has been hospitalized. I assure you it's valid information. This is not the first time I have passed on information, is it? That tiffin is at least 5 kg of solid gold studded with diamonds,' Sajid whined.

'How do you know? Are you quoting from *The Siasat Daily*?' Idris asked suspiciously.

'Saab, I have seen it with my own eyes. This guy has the tiffin. It looks exactly like the one they showed on TV after the theft,' Sajid said confidently.

'Okay, let me see what I can do. Now, tell me who the thief that stole the tiffin is.'

'Saab, I want the money before I open my mouth.'

'Do you want me to take you in lockup and get a confession from you? I can charge you as an accessory to the theft. Do you want me to do that? I told you that you will be paid a good amount. Now, tell me—who is it?' Madhu ordered.

'He is my distant relative. His name is Khooni Badshah. His friend, Ghulam, is also involved in the theft.'

'Khooni Badshah!' Idris exclaimed. The police knew

all about Badshah. Khooni Badshah, as his friends and acquaintances called him, was a notorious thief and an occasional construction worker who had 17 burglary cases pending against him.

'Saab, Badshah tried to sell the items in Mumbai but failed,' Sajid informed them.

'Okay, we will get back to you. Keep your phone close to you,' Madhu said as they turned their bike around to drive to the police station to update their boss.

'Sir, this seems to be a good lead to follow. Badshah's MO is burglary and he is a construction worker. Remember the perfect arrows that the thieves had drawn in the museum?' Constable Idris excitedly reminded Inspector Madhu.

'Yes, I think that Badshah could be the thief,' the Inspector agreed.

Madhu met Chaitanya Kumar, who was in his office at the police station and explained the situation to him. 'We have a very promising lead in the museum theft case. My informant tells me that Badshah, a notorious burglar, may be involved. He is trying to sell a tiffin box stolen from The Nizam's Museum. Immediately after the theft, Badshah and his partner had gone to Mumbai to sell the items. Failing to do so, they have come back to Hyderabad and are trying to sell them here.'

'Are you sure about this?' ACP Chaitanya asked cautiously.

'Yes, Sir. This Sajid is a distant relative of Badshah's. Sajid himself is a rowdy sheeter, and Badshah trusts him. I'm confident that this information is genuine.'

'Okay, let's go and meet the Commissioner,' Chaitanya said, asking one of the constables to get the police car allocated to him.

The Commissioner was equally excited when this

information was given to him. Here was the breakthrough he had been hoping for. He was determined that the criminals should be caught red-handed with the stolen artefacts.

'Let's do this extremely carefully. We will send two people from our IT team to set up CCTV cameras at Sajid's place. And we will use folks from the city security team to recce the informer's house and all the entry and exit routes.'

'Why, Sir?' ACP Chaitanya asked.

'So that, in case the thief is able to escape from the house despite the police presence, there will be policemen in plain-clothes or what we call cut-off parties to grab him.'

'No, Sir, I understand why we need to plan for the cut-off parties. My question is why do we need to involve the city security team? Aren't we good enough?'

'Come on, use your brains, Chaitanya!' the Commissioner snapped, 'The task force has been exposed to the public of the Old City. They may be recognized. The city security team is better. They only take care of the security of VIPs and are not exposed to the public in general.'

'Okay, Sir,' ACP Chaitanya agreed grudgingly.

'I'll get somebody from the city security team to pose as a customer. That way, the thief will not get suspicious. I suggest we arrange a suitcase with cash. Around ₹10 lakh will be sufficient, I think.'

'Madhu, are you taking notes?' the Commissioner asked.

'Yes, Sir. First, we'll identify a person from the city security team who will go and recce the informer's home and identify spots where the CCTV cameras will be placed,' Madhu replied.

'Yes, take the help of Srikanth from the city security team. I'll update him and he'll expect a call from you. Also, take

SI Noor Begum. She can go in a plain dress and burka and scout the area around Sajid's home to identify the positions for the cut-off parties.'

'Yes, Sir, good idea. People in that area would be less suspicious of a woman in a burka.'

'Wait. Let me pull Raja into this meeting. He sits on the second floor. He will be responsible for setting up the CCTV cameras.'

They all waited tensely for Raja to arrive. Would they finally be able to get the items back? The Commissioner was particularly tired of the negative feedback that the press was regularly dishing out. Once Raja, a short thin man with a huge bald head and black-framed glasses arrived, the Commissioner updated him about the case and their plans. 'You'll go with Srikanth from the city security team and install the CCTV cameras. Ensure that the video is recorded as well as transmitted directly to my office.'

After the meeting, Madhu called Sajid. 'Somebody from the police team will come to your home to set up CCTV cameras.'

'Saab...saab, don't do that!' Sajid said, panicking. 'People might get suspicious. Most of my neighbours seem to have no work other than watching what's happening in other people's homes!'

'Don't worry, our men will be in plain-clothes and pose as TV repair technicians. You have a TV, no? You told me you had seen the gold tiffin on TV,' Madhu ended the call, ignoring Sajid's protests.

The next day, Srikanth and Raja went to Sajid's home. It was one of the better homes in a core Muslim colony among the hillocks of Rajendra Nagar. There was a tiny semi-open courtyard where water and some junk items were stored. A half-open door led to a tiny room with blue, fading paint. As they stood outside, waiting for Sajid to come out, they saw that folks from the adjacent houses were looking at them.

'TV repair *ke liye aye* (We have come to repair the TV),' Srikanth said loudly as Sajid came out of the door.

'*Hau aiye...* (Yes, please come in),' Sajid said.

They entered the room with the tiny TV unit and a tattered sofa set. Two toddlers were playing on the floor, their toys scattered around them. They could see a tiny kitchen and an adjacent bathroom from the sitting room. A woman was cooking meat in the kitchen and its delicious aroma was wafting out.

'Where will the party sit?' Srikanth asked in a low voice. The walls were thin and he was worried that the neighbours would be able to hear them. Quickly and efficiently, Raja and Srikanth worked together and identified the spots where three cameras would be set up.

Meanwhile, Sajid sat on the floor with the ancient TV set and opened its back cover. If anybody walked in, the men would sit down near the open TV set and pretend to repair it. Luckily for them, nobody came in. Within half an hour, their work was done and they quickly exited that area, taking two close-up photos of Ghulam and Badshah provided by Sajid.

Noor Begum arrived at the house around 1.00 p.m., pretending to sell Tupperware products, and recced the area to identify the cut-off routes. The next day was to be the big day, when the meeting between the 'customer' and Khooni Badshah had been set up.

That evening, the Commissioner called one final meeting, in the control centre, with the team that he had formed for nabbing the criminals. A Google map was displayed on the projector screen so that the entry and exit paths to Sajid's house were clearly visible. Everybody was excited and nervous and adrenaline was running high.

Inspectors Zain, Srikanth and Raja were present, along with Constables Noor Begum, Mohsin, Laraib and Kamran. They were all from the city security team, except for Raja. Inspector Madhu, ACP Chaitanya, Constables Idris and Krishna completed the team. Additionally, two burly constables, Rana and Vikram, were also present for the meeting. The Commissioner had deliberately kept the team small to prevent any leak of information. As per the Commissioner's instructions, before coming to the meeting, they had all gotten an approximate idea about where Sajid's home was located. A WhatsApp group had also been formed, allowing the team to communicate and keep each other in the loop.

Mohsin, Laraib and Kamran had already recced the area extensively and noted the spots identified by Noor Begum. They would remain at these spots to ensure that the criminals would not get away, even if they managed to escape the police from inside the house. The team was given close-ups of Khooni Badshah and Ghulam and was asked to memorize each feature of both the men so that they could monitor their approach.

'You will use signals to communicate with each other or message each other via your mobile phones. Laraib and Kamran would be able to see each other, but Mohsin will be standing where the road turns and hence, will not be visible to them,' the Commissioner said, pointing to the map on the projector to communicate his point better. 'Mohsin will need to rely totally on his cell phone to communicate with the others. Clear so far?'

The team nodded.

'Laraib and Kamran, if you spot Badshah approaching, you will signal this by wiping your face with your handkerchief. In case you don't see him, signal by scratching your head. Clear so far? We cannot afford to make any mistakes,' the Commissioner said.

'Yes, Sir,' the two men said in unison.

'Zain, you will pose as the customer. Are you confident you can pull it off?'

Inspector Zain nodded. He was an elderly, extremely fair-skinned, good-looking individual, who had once aspired to be an actor. He looked less like a police officer and more like a scholarly Muslim gentleman. He wore gold-framed spectacles and had a small, hennaed beard, which added to his personality. He had once performed a skit in one of the annual police functions and the Commissioner had been impressed with his acting skills. Now, he planned to tap into these skills.

He looked appraisingly at Zain, who seemed nervous. 'Don't be so nervous,' the Commissioner said in a gentle voice. 'I still remember the skit that you did during the annual day police function. You can do it. Trust me.'

The Commissioner's encouraging and soothing words gave Zain strength and he nodded his head. He looked less tense and more confident.

Turning to Chaitanya and Madhu, the Commissioner said, 'After the meeting, Raja is going to provide us with a dongle for Wi-Fi connection. Madhu, you will keep it switched on in your pocket. You will also check that the Wi-Fi is working properly as soon as you reach Sajid's place tomorrow. Raja, you will need to be on standby. If anything goes wrong, you will need to help.'

'Of course, Sir. I will be here in the office by 6.00 a.m. tomorrow,' Raja responded promptly.

'Good, I'll also be here,' the Commissioner said, looked at Madhu and continued, 'Raja has set up the cameras in such a way that they will automatically connect to the Wi-Fi once the dongle is switched on. Is that clear?'

Madhu nodded.

The Commissioner turned back to Inspector Zain. 'I'll provide you with a private BMW car to go to Sajid's house tomorrow. There will be a briefcase with ₹10 lakh in that car. Clear so far?' the Commissioner asked, looking penetratingly at him.

'Yes, Sir,' Zain said, trying to make his voice steady and confident.

The Commissioner turned to Rana and Vikram and said, 'Vikram, you will drive the car and Rana will remain in the trunk of the BMW. You will focus on the criminals at all times and ensure that he can't escape, okay?'

Vikram and Rana nodded respectfully. Then, they looked at each other and smiled slightly. They usually worked as a team. They were looking forward to this adventure.

'Now, Inspector Madhu, ACP Chaitanya and constables Krishna and Idris, you will go in plain-clothes and hide inside the house. You'll need to be very fast so that people don't recognize you. Try to reach separately, not in a group. You can go by 5.30 a.m., as not many people will be around at that time. As soon as you know that Badshah is approaching, Madhu and Chaitanya will hide inside the bathroom. Krishna and Idris, you will hide in the kitchen,' the Commissioner instructed.

Krishna nodded grimly. He was tall and muscular and was known in the police force for his immense strength.

'Did you ask Sajid's wife and children to move out of the home?' the Commissioner asked as the thought struck him suddenly.

'Yes, Sir. It has been taken care of. We asked him to send his family to his in-laws' house,' Inspector Madhu said.

'Good, good. Okay, now, there can be two scenarios, Zain. Badshah will either come with the box or he won't. Let's hope and pray that he'll come with the box because then it'll become easy for us. As soon as he takes out the box, Zain, you'll cross your arms in front of you. I'll be watching the video from my office and Madhu and Chaitanya on their mobiles. If we see this signal, we will know that it's time to take Badshah. Clear so far?'

'Yes, Sir. What's the other possible scenario?' Zain asked.

'Yes, the other scenario is a trickier and more likely one. Badshah may not come with the box, as he might suspect a trap. If that is the case, you'll need to take out your spectacles and keep them on the sofa beside you to let the others know that the box is not with Badshah. You'll then need to strike a deal with him. Maybe you can hand him the briefcase with the cash and send him in the car to his home or wherever he has stashed the booty. Vikram and Rana will be responsible for ensuring that Badshah doesn't run away and comes back to Sajid's place with the tiffin. Another car will follow you and recover the money from Badshah as soon as he hands over the tiffin box to Zain,' the Commissioner elaborated.

'Has the other car been organized?' Madhu asked.

'Yes, my PA Haleem is organizing the cash and the two cars,' the Commissioner replied.

'Okay, Sir,' Madhu said.

'Now, Zain, coming back to you, Badshah might say that

he needs some time to get the box if he has hidden the booty with someone far away from Hyderabad, maybe in Mumbai. Then, we will allow him to go away with the cash, but we will set up 24/7 surveillance on him. Your role is crucial. You will need to play it extremely convincingly,' the Commissioner said.

'Does he know how much he will be paid?' Zain asked.

'Initially, ₹2 crore, and after the tiffin has been authenticated in the international market, you will pay him ₹3 crore more. That's what Sajid has told Badshah. Is that correct Madhu?' the Commissioner asked.

As Madhu and Idris had already updated Sajid about the plans, Madhu nodded his head in the affirmative to the Commissioner's query.

'So, everybody is clear on their roles here, correct?' the Commissioner asked.

The team nodded.

'Okay then, all the best for tomorrow,' the Commissioner concluded the meeting.

Inspector Madhu went to bed as soon as he reached home. He knew that he would need to wake up by 3.00 a.m. and get ready. An unmarked police car would drop him, Chaitanya, Idris and Krishna about 1 km from Sajid's home by 4.30 a.m. From there, they would need to walk. Sajid would leave his door open but keep the lights off so that they could enter noiselessly without arousing the suspicion of any nosy neighbours.

Madhu's wife wasn't happy about this plan. Since the time of the theft, Madhu had hardly spent any time at home. Now, she would have to wake up by 3.00 a.m. and prepare breakfast for him. She was utterly fed up.

'I don't know why I married you!' she grumbled.

12

THE CAPTURE

Inspector Madhu had found it difficult to fall asleep the previous night so he nearly overslept on the big day. However, his wife gently woke him up with a cup of fresh, fragrant filter coffee and steaming hot idlis and sambar.

Looking at her, he felt a twinge of regret. *I'm a bad husband. I truly don't appreciate her. I'll take her to Goa after this case is solved*, he promised himself. But, right now, he had extremely important work to be completed—the recovery of the artefacts stolen from The Nizam's Museum.

Like Madhu, Zain, too, had spent a sleepless night. He looked at the watch glowing on the bedside table. It was 1.00 a.m.! Light was filtering out of his son's bedroom. As a software engineer, working in a multinational IT organization, he was still working, probably coordinating with his American counterpart.

Zain closed his eyes and took deep, calming breaths. His head was aching. Switching on the small table lamp by his side, he took some ayurvedic ointment from his bedside table and applied it on his forehead. He loved the strong, menthol odour of the ointment. The sting of the balm made his eyes water, but, soon, his headache got better. He needed to rest. He checked once again if he had set the alarm for 7.00 a.m. correctly. He went over in his mind about what he would say to Khooni Badshah to ensure that he was captured with the loot. He had heard that counting sheep helped one fall asleep but it didn't do him any good. He knew that he had a crucial role to play in the elaborate plan that the police had made to catch the thief. Would he be able to perform his role convincingly? He was a widower and lived with his 22-year-old son, who had just started working. His son had very little time to spare, and Zain didn't want to burden him with his apprehensions. He wished his wife were alive to listen to his worries and appreciate the big role he was about to play today. She had always done so when she had been alive. He missed her. He sighed and turned to his side, trying to sleep.

Finally, it was 4.30 a.m. A testing time for Anjani Kumar's best team, entrusted with the crucial task of recovering the artefacts from The Nizam's Museum—an important part of India's heritage.

Madhu, Chaitanya, Idris and Krishna were dropped off at a place as close to Sajid's home as possible in an unmarked police car. One by one, they stealthily entered his house and sat down in silence. Madhu and Chaitanya checked if the CCTV cameras were in place, switched on the dongle and confirmed that the pictures were being transmitted to their mobiles. The Commissioner and Raja, who was in charge of the IT team, personally coordinated with them and checked that the video was being transmitted to the Commissioner's office screen along with being recorded.

By the time they finished checking everything, it was already 7.00 a.m. Sajid made them cups of really bad but piping hot tea. The four policemen sipped the tea and counted the minutes.

The private BMW, which the Commissioner had arranged, came to pick up Zain at 10.00 a.m. Sajid lived around half an hour away. Badshah was supposed to meet them at 11.00 a.m. Vikram was driving the car and Rana moved reluctantly from the passenger seat to the trunk. Luckily, nobody was around in the basement and this activity was done smoothly. The trunk was not closed tightly so that Rana could breathe. The car had been fitted with a GPS device. This would allow the police to monitor the movement of the car. If Badshah did not bring the artefacts with him, Zain would offer him his car to go to the place where the booty had been hidden. Vikram would then drive Badshah to the place where the artefacts were stashed and the police would track the movement via the GPS device of the car.

Zain sat down inside the plush, perfumed interior and touched the smooth leather seat with his hands. The seat felt cool and luxurious. He had never ridden in a BMW before. He was wearing his best and most expensive pathan suit. Vikram looked at Zain and said with an encouraging smile, 'You are looking royal.'

Zain felt slightly reassured. He looked the part then. He had wondered if he had over-dressed and had wanted to check with his son, but he had still been sleeping after working late into the night, and Zain had not wanted to wake him up. Instead, he had left the house, shutting the front door softly behind him to not disturb his son.

He checked the briefcase kept by his side. It was heavy and full of money. *Good, everything is set. Now it's all up to me*, he thought. Again, his palms started sweating. He took deep breaths to calm himself down. His mobile phone pinged. It was a message from the Commissioner.

```
Everything has been set up properly, don't worry.
We are all with you. Best of luck.
```

Zain felt himself perking up. He texted back:

```
Thank you, Sir!
```

As they neared Sajid's house, they drove past Mohsin, who was wearing a shabby, faded, grey pathan suit. He was leaning against a wall and reading a newspaper. He blended in really well with the locality. He noticed the car and looked at Zain, poker-faced. Then, he scratched his head to indicate that Badshah had not yet arrived.

The car could not go all the way up to Sajid's house, as the road was too narrow. Taking the briefcase in his hand, Zain quickly walked through the narrow lane leading to Sajid's home. He was reassured when he saw Kamran sitting in a café nearby. He also spotted Laraib standing closer to Sajid's home. He was amazed to see how well they blended into their surroundings. He hoped that he would be able to play his role just as convincingly. His hands were so sweaty, he was worried that the heavy briefcase would slip from his grip. He took deep, calming breaths and walked faster. He knocked softly when he reached Sajid's door. Sajid immediately opened it and locked it after him.

As soon as Zain saw his colleagues, he felt calmer. With so many of them around, there was very little chance that things could go wrong. Madhu showed him where the CCTV cameras were placed and assured him that everything was working well.

'No need to feel tensed, we are all here to help you,' ACP Chaitanya reassured him, arranging the briefcase on a small table in front of the sofa. 'You open the briefcase and show the money to Badshah. But do avoid giving it to him before he hands over the stolen items.'

Zain nodded. 'Yes, yes, of course.'

Then, a WhatsApp message flashed across all their mobile screen. It was from Mohsin. It read:

Target approaching.

'That reminds me,' ACP Chaitanya said, 'keep your phones on silent!'

The men scrambled to take up positions. Zain sat down on the sofa, his heart thumping.

Soon, there was a soft knock on Sajid's door. It was Badshah.

'*Arre, aao miyaan*, look who is waiting for you,' Sajid said with a wide smile.

Badshah was a strong young man with a dark complexion and curly hair. He was wearing a flashy silk shirt and tight pants. He did not have a beard. The smell of cheap aftershave filled the room. He had seen the BMW parked on the way to Sajid's home and had been reassured that Sajid had found a worthy party.

He stood near the door and said, 'As-salaam alaikum, Saab!'

Zain was also reassured to see that Badshah was carrying a bulging backpack. Zain hoped that it was the real tiffin. 'Walaikum as-salaam,' he replied, pretending to be affable.

'Sit here,' Sajid said, patting a plastic chair close to the sofa. Badshah nodded and sat down, wiping his face. He was also nervous and sweating profusely.

'Have you got the tiffin?' Sajid asked. 'This is Farid saab. I told you about him, right? He deals in antique items. He says he will pay ₹2 crore immediately for the goods. After he sells them in the international market, he will pay the rest of the money.'

'Okay, show me the money,' Badshah said.

Zain opened the briefcase and showed him the cash inside.

Though Badshah's eyes shone at the sight of the money, he was suspicious. 'This does not look like ₹2 crore,' he said.

'Arre miyaan, Farid saab is not stupid. He will not come here with all that money, right? Once he sees the items and is convinced that they are authentic, he will take us to his home in Banjara Hills, where he will hand over the rest of the cash. Chalo, show him the items,' Sajid intervened.

Badshah reluctantly took out the tiffin, the cup and the saucer. Zain sucked in his breath. The gold box glittered in the artificial light. The diamond-encrusted lid seemed to twinkle at him. Then, he took the cup and saucer. The cup was small but studded with big emeralds and rubies. He had no doubt that the artefacts were real.

In retrospect, Inspector Madhu described the moment as: 'To our amazement, the spectacular gold tiffin box appeared to be intact as were the cup and the saucer encrusted with rubies and emeralds. We immediately knew that we were looking at the items stolen from The Nizam's Museum.'

Zain folded his hands across his chest, giving the signal that the thief could be nabbed. Immediately, Madhu, Chaitanya, Idris and Krishna shot out from their hiding places and jumped on Badshah. It took four men to overpower Badshah, who was struggling and swearing at Sajid at the same time.

After handcuffing him, the men looked at the artefacts again, struggling for breath. Madhu, who had studied the photos of the stolen items very carefully, was the first person to note that the diamonds encrusted on the box were missing.

'Where are the diamonds?' he snarled at Badshah.

By then, Chaitanya also noted that the ruby- and emerald-studded gold spoon was missing.

'Where is the spoon, madarchod?' ACP Chaitanya demanded angrily.

Badshah was terrified by this time. 'It's with my partner, Ghulam,' he stammered.

'Where is he?' ACP Chaitanya asked.

'In Rajendra Nagar only, near the petrol pump, Sir,' Badshah replied meekly.

'Look, if you lead us to him, we will help you. If you don't, and Ghulam escapes with the diamond, he will become rich and you will languish in jail for years. Do you want that?' Chaitanya threatened.

Badshah nodded to indicate that he would cooperate while glowering with hatred at Sajid.

Chaitanya called the Commissioner with the update. 'Some of the artefacts are missing. He says they're with his partner, Ghulam, who stays nearby.'

'Ask Badshah to call Ghulam. Set a trap for him. Badshah should tell Ghulam that he is coming to his house to meet him.'

Badshah cooperated with the police and made the call. Quickly, the police team set off towards Ghulam's house in the car allocated to Zain. They did not want to delay lest Ghulam smell a rat and get away.

Badshah was handcuffed and bundled in another unmarked police car with Vikram and Rana keeping a close eye on him once the car reached close to Ghulam's place. Badshah directed the police to Ghulam's home. Inspector Madhu and ACP Chaitanya got down, covered the remaining distance on foot and knocked on Ghulam's door while the rest of the police team lurked nearby.

Zeenat opened the door and looked up at Madhu and Chaitanya, both of whom were tall men. Their demeanour and physical appearance told her that they were not from that area. She became apprehensive. *Who were they? What did they want? Had they knocked on her door by mistake?*

Outwardly, she maintained her composure. 'What do you want?' she asked.

'We would like to speak to Ghulam,' Inspector Madhu responded.

Zeenat immediately knew that Ghulam was in trouble. He had been acting strangely lately. He was always tense and wouldn't tell her why he had been absent from home for the past few days. By this time, Ghulam, who had been inside the room, out of sight of the police, had become aware that things had gone wrong. He hid under the bed and tried to call Badshah. But Badshah's phone had been switched off by the police.

'He...he is not at home,' Zeenat said, trying to slam the door in their faces.

But Madhu's foot was already on the threshold preventing her from closing the door. They barged in. Other members of the police team also crowded in. Inside, there was a tiny bedroom and Ghulam was nowhere to be seen. Then, a mobile phone rang and was abruptly switched off. Madhu realized that the sound had come from beneath the bed. He bent down and saw Ghulam hiding there. Ghulam didn't resist as he was pulled out and handcuffed. He was a thin, young lad who was terrified at the sight of so many policemen. He quickly handed over the diamonds and the gold spoon.

The momentous arrest, made after days of extreme hard work and due diligence by the Hyderabad Police, was quiet, without any fanfare. Badshah and Ghulam surrendered without so much as a whimper.

Like the robbery, the recovery of the artefacts, which were returned to the museum and kept back on display, also dominated the news. The publicity was, in a way, good for the museum, as many people visited to gawk at the priceless heirlooms. The media—*The Hindu*[26], *The Economic Times*[27] and even international newspapers like *The Guardian* from the UK[28]—were all praises for the Hyderabad Police, who had solved this most challenging case in record time.

However, doubts were raised regarding the authenticity of the stolen artefacts as reported in the *Deccan Chronicle*[29]. The photo of the teacup that was circulated after the theft did not match the actual cup that was recovered. The stolen cup had no design except for embedded rubies. The photo that was mistakenly circulated as being stolen had an exquisite design.

[26]Nanisetti, Serish, 'Hyderabad Nizam Museum Theft Case: Police Recover Antique Items, Arrest Two', *The Hindu*, 11 September 2018, https://bit.ly/3DwusMJ. Accessed on 19 September 2022.

[27]'Thief Used Hyderabad Nizam's Gold Tiffin Box to Eat Every Day', *The Economic Times*, 11 September 2018, https://bit.ly/3DyuUKg. Accessed on 19 September 2022.

[28]Safi, Michael, 'Indian Men Accused of Stealing Gold Tiffin Box "Ate Their Lunch Out of It"', *The Guardian*, 12 September 2018, https://bit.ly/3SUTdq8. Accessed on 20 September 2022.

[29]Suares, Coreena and Naveen Kumar, 'Nizam Museum Theft: Doubts Over Gold Cup Raised and Rested', *Deccan Chronicle*, 12 September 2018, https://bit.ly/3djtsRu. Accessed on 19 September 2022.

These doubts were soon nullified.

The fears of the police that the artefacts might have fallen into the hands of a criminal mastermind or a millionaire collector residing in Europe or America were laid to rest. The beautiful works of art had never strayed too far from Hyderabad, their rightful home. After always being used by the royalty, they had, for the first time, seen the seedier side of Hyderabad and had even been used by two petty criminals.

The picture of the wrong cup that was circulated in the media
Source: The Hyderabad Police

Badshah and Ghulam cooperated fully with the Hyderabad Police. They were not romantic dreamers, rapacious art collectors or avant-garde artists. Except for the fact that they had stolen Hyderabad's cultural heritage, they were thoroughly inconsequential men, petty criminals. The story they told after their capture was stranger than fiction. They had stolen the artefacts and lived their dream of living like badshahs by eating their meals from the gold tiffin. However, it had been a short-lived dream.

The artefacts are back in their rightful place in the Nizam's old palace, the Purani Haveli.

EPILOGUE:
What Happened to the Nizam's Legacy?

The epoch of the princely states of India effectively ended with the country's Independence in August 1947. By 1950, almost all of the principalities had acceded to either India or Pakistan. However, the seventh Nizam of Hyderabad, Mir Osman Ali Khan, who was among the richest princes in pre-Independence India, refused to join either India or Pakistan. He hired Sir Walter Monckton, one of the smartest lawyers in England, to stop the Indian government from forcing him to accede. Monckton thrashed out a 'Standstill Agreement' between the Nizam and the Government of India.[30]

While these negotiations were happening, the Nizam announced that he intended to purchase weapons to safeguard the landlocked state of Hyderabad. The money for this purchase, which had been kept in the Imperial Bank of India, was shifted to the Hyderabad Government's accounts in other banks in the UK. One of these accounts had £1,007,940.45. This account was controlled by the Nizam's

[30]K. Venkateshwarlu, 'How the Nizam Lost Hyderabad in 1948', *The Hindu*, 14 August 2012, https://bit.ly/3BQ4IcI. Accessed on 19 September 2022.

Foreign Minister Moin Nawaz Jung.[31]

Considering the emerging situation in Hyderabad and to safeguard the interests of the independent princely state, on 15 September 1948, Jung wrote to Pakistan's High Commissioner, Habib Ibrahim Rahimtoola, stating that he would like to transfer £1 million into Rahimtoola's account. This amount was, at that time, lying at the credit of the Nizam's government in the National Westminster Bank (NatWest), London. He requested the High Commissioner to keep the amount in a trust.

On 16 September 1948, Jung called on Rahimtoola in the UK and asked him to accept the funds in the presence of Pakistan's Foreign Minister Muhammad Zafrullah Khan. This led to the funds being transferred to Rahimtoola's account on 20 September 1948.

In the meantime, on 17 September 1948, the Nizam's army went to war with the Indian Army. They surrendered to India after 105 hours of battle. After surrendering, the Nizam wired the Governor-General and the Deputy Prime Minister of India, asking for the money given to Rahimtoola to be transferred back to his account in the NatWest. However, the bank refused.

In 1950, The Government of India made a claim on the Nizam's money lying in a trust of the Pakistan High Commissioner in the NatWest, London. The Pakistan government refused to comply and asked the NatWest to transfer the money to the new Pakistan High Commissioner, M.A.H. Ispahani, in 1953. In response, in 1954, the Government

---

[31]Nanisetti, Serish, 'Explained | Who Gets to Own the Nizam's Millions?' *The Hindu*, 6 October 2019, https://bit.ly/3BRiXy2. Accessed on 19 September 2022.

of India sued Jung, Rahimtoola and the bank to recover the money. In the court case, Pakistan relied on the meeting between Jung, Rahimtoola and Muhammad Zafrullah Khan. The judge supported the exchange of letters a day prior to the meeting.

The case dragged on till 1956, when the Chancery Division judge, Justice Upjohn ruled: 'The present transaction was an intergovernmental transaction: let it be solved by inter-governmental negotiations.'[32] However, Pakistan refused to negotiate, claiming sovereign immunity. The Government of India, then, moved to the Court of Appeals in the UK the same year. In the Court of Appeals, three judges ruled in favour of the Nizam, i.e., India. 'That the transfer was effected [...] without any authority from the Nizam.'[33] However, there was a setback for India in 1957 when five judges of the House of Lords overturned the Court of Appeals' decision. The judgement gave Pakistan sovereign immunity. Because of this immunity, Pakistan couldn't be sued in England. Hence, the money remained locked up in the NatWest.

In 1960, the Prime Minister of India Jawaharlal Nehru and the President of Pakistan Ayub Khan negotiated behind the scenes and agreed to split the money in a 60:40 ratio. This happened on the sidelines of diplomatic negotiations between India and Pakistan on the Indus Water Treaty, facilitated by the World Bank. In 1963, the seventh Nizam initiated a payment in which the Bank of Nova Scotia Company (Bahamas) was chosen as the trustee of the fund for his two grandsons and family. The Nova Scotia Bank filed papers and became a third

---

[32]Ibid.
[33]Ibid.

party in the fund—the other two parties being India, as an inheritor state, and Pakistan.

In 1965, the Nizam assigned his claim to the fund to the Government of India. In 1983, India and Pakistan jointly submitted a letter claiming the money to the NatWest. However, the Nova Scotia Bank put a spanner in the arrangement by claiming that this arrangement was not acceptable. In 2013, Pakistan cast off its claim of sovereign protection and made an unqualified claim on the fund. They argued that arms were supplied to the Nizam in lieu of the money. However, this argument was rejected by Judge Marcus Smith of the High Court of England and Wales and, in October 2019, the UK court ruled that the money must go to the descendants of the Nizam.

In this way, one of the world's longest-running legal battles for the Nizam's great wealth, now estimated to be £35 million, or about ₹306 crore, came to an end on 2 October 2019. Subsequently, the descendants of seventh Nizam of Hyderabad and India could collect £35 million from London's NatWest.[34] The judge also referred to an agreement between the Government of India and the princes about how the money would be divided. The details of the agreement are not available.

∽

The Nizam VII had 18 sons and 16 daughters. The current Nizam VIII[35], Mukarram Jah, lives in Turkey. He has transferred

---

[34]Ibid.
[35]Titular title

his interest in the fund to Hillview Assets Holdings Limited. His brother, Prince Muffakam Jah, was an important witness, whose evidence was relied on by the judge to reach his verdict.

While most of the royal relics of the Asaf Jahis, who ruled over Hyderabad between 1724 and 1948, have disappeared, Mukarram Jah's former wife, Princess Esra Jah, has renovated two palaces in Hyderabad. The Falaknuma Palace, with its faux Gothic and Roman elements, has been converted into a super luxury hotel. It includes one of the longest dining tables that can seat 101 people and has a breathtaking view of Hyderabad. The Chowmahalla Palace, where Mukarram Jah, the Nizam VIII was crowned, has been opened to tourists.

Mukarram Jah leads a private life. He has spent some years in Australia and later, in Turkey, indulging in his fancy for machines that range from sleek cars to earthmovers. A few of his earthmovers can still be seen in the Chowmahalla Palace. The other palaces owned by him are Nazribagh Palace, Naukhanda Palace in Aurangabad and the Purani Haveli, where the Mukarram Jah Trust for Education and Learning is located.

Though the Nizam's inheritance now legally belongs to his heirs, there is a legal tussle going on among his current heirs for this inheritance. Nawab Najaf Ali Khan, another grandson of the seventh Nizam, met the police commissioner of Hyderabad and submitted a complaint, along with supporting documents, alleging that Prince Mukarram Jah, his ex-wife Princess Esra (who also holds the general power of attorney for Prince Mukarram Jah) and his son Azmet Jah, have used false documents in the UK High Court to lay claim to the

Nizam's fund worth £35 million lying in NatWest Bank there.[36]

The Commissioner, along with Additional CP Crimes Shikha Goel, the Detective Department and task force officials, were congratulated by Prince Muffakham Jah.

Source: The Hyderabad Police

After the successful solution of the case, Hyderabad City Police Commissioner Anjani Kumar and his team members were felicitated by Prince Muffakham Jah at The Nizam's Museum. Later, Prince Muffakham Jah spoke to the media and appreciated the work done by the Hyderabad police in tracing the artefacts stolen from the museum.[37]

---

[36]Special Correspondent, 'VII Nizam's Grandson Moves Police Against Two Cousins, Two Other Kin', *The Hindu*, 17 November 2020, https://bit.ly/3dn08th. Accessed on 19 September 2022.

[37]'Prince Muffakham Jah Lauds Hyderabad Cops', *The Hans india*, 29 December 2018, https://bit.ly/3G60AL8. Accessed on 8 November 2022.

ABOUT COMMISSIONER ANJANI KUMAR

The former Hyderabad Police Commissioner Anjani Kumar

Source: The Hyderabad Police

Anjani Kumar is the Director General of Police. He was the commissioner of Hyderabad, a metropolitan city in India with a population of over 9 million people, when the heist at The Nizam's Museum occurred. He successfully spearheaded the operation to recover the stolen artefacts.

Anjani Kumar is an IPS officer, Telangana cadre, of the 1990 batch. He has been awarded the United Nations (UN) Peace Medal twice while serving with the UN in Bosnia. He is an alumnus of Kirori Mal College, Delhi University, and St. Xavier's High School, Patna. During his training at the Sardar Vallabhbhai Patel National Police Academy, he won the Maharaja of Tonk Cup for the best horse rider and the R.D. Singh Cup for being the best swimmer of his batch.

In the early 90s, he was first posted as assistant superintendent of police in the Jangaon subdivision of Warangal District. Naxalites welcomed the young officer with a blast at the Jangaon Railway Station. He was faced with challenges from his first day of duty in the most affected parts of Warangal district. He effectively handled extremism in the district by developing various strategies to control the extremists. His tactics helped protect government properties and precious lives of innocent, law-abiding citizens in Warangal.

Later, he also worked as the superintendent of police (SP), Guntur district, bordering the dense Nallamala forest, which was notorious for Naxal activity. He dealt with the extremism at its peak in northern Telangana and guided the newly appointed IPS cadres and SPs during his posting as deputy inspector general of police (DIG), Nizamabad Range.

He handled the tough job of conducting anti-terror operations in the Intelligence Wing during his tenure as DIG. He also secured the hypersensitive Hyderabad city when communal tensions were at their peak, especially in the Old City. Intelligence inputs were effectively shared to maintain peace and harmony at the world-famous Charminar and its surrounding areas. He also personally visited many sensitive places to assess the ground reality.

He was then promoted to inspector general (IG) of Police in the North Zone of the united Andhra Pradesh. The region was considered the defensive wall of the united Andhra Pradesh, as it borders the hotbeds of red terror—the Naxal-affected Gadchiroli District in Maharashtra and the Dandakaranya area of Chhattisgarh. He had the tough task of guiding the SPs and the officers on special duty (OSDs) and coordinating the special parties during his tenure as IG.

Another herculean task he undertook was handling the separate Telangana agitation. Several protests, suicides by the youth and the subsequent processions demanding separate statehood had been the order of the day. He was later posted to Hyderabad as additional commissioner of police, law and order. Managing law and order in Hyderabad immediately after the formation of the state of Telangana was a huge challenge. However, it was very effectively handled during his tenure.

Subsequently, he was promoted to the post of additional director general (Law and Order), the second-in-charge after the director general of police. He handled the security arrangements for Ivanka Trump and coordinated the security for the Global Entrepreneur Summit, 2017, a prestigious business event held in Hyderabad.

Later, he was posted as the commissioner of police, Hyderabad—a top job in the Hyderabad police force. Very few officers of the esteemed IPS get the opportunity to become the Kotwal of Shehar-e-Hyderabad. Here, too, he was welcomed by the sensational case of dacoity at an Old City gold shop.

Anjani Kumar has had the opportunity to visit world-class agencies like the FBI, CIA, French Police and Berlin Police. He has also participated in many international workshops and conferences and made a presentation as part of a meeting with the New York City Police. He has co-authored the coffee table book *Journey of the Hyderabad City Police* with Noopur Kumar.

214 • *The Arlington's ...*

...with the two of you. Go, follow...

'We are looking for Shakeel bhai.'

'He's at the back of the store.' Obviously, the man had been expecting them.

He got up from the chair and flicked a switch. The dim shop lit up and they saw that it was a long shop, full of items on both sides, separated by a narrow aisle leading to the back of the shop. At the far end of the shop was a narrow alcove, and they could see that it led to another room.

As they followed the man to the back of the shop, Badshah and Ghulam felt like they were inside Aladdin's cave. The shop was full of statues, lamps, old clocks, gramophones, records and musical instruments. Badshah was sure that there would be items stolen from rich homes in Mumbai and other areas that had found their way into this shop.

They entered a bigger room beyond the alcove with green walls, some mismatched sofas and tables covered with lace tablecloths. An expensive-looking carpet covered the floor. The room was air-conditioned. A man in his early forties, dressed in a kurta-pyjama, was sitting in a rocking chair next to the sofas. He had a well-groomed beard and cold eyes lined with black kohl. The smell of attar wafted in the air.

Ashraf bowed to the man. 'As-salaam alaikum, Shakeel bhai,' he said, in a deferential voice. 'We have got something special for you.'

The man guided them to the nearest sofa with a lazy wave of his hands. 'Tell me, what have you got?' he asked in a curiously soft whispering voice. Ghulam and Badshah somehow felt extremely scared of this man.